Adams,
Romp Herd £2

# THE
## *Compleat*
# RANCHER

# THE
# *Compleat*
# RANCHER

## RUSSELL H. BENNETT

*With Drawings by*
## ROSS SANTEE

*TO MIRIAM,*
*GRACIOUS WIFE AND HELPMEET*

# Introduction

Many inquiries have come to us of late about cattle ranching, and what it has to offer as a career. It seemed worth while to attempt to answer these inquiries collectively, and so this book was written. It is the season-to-season and job-to-job story of a cattle ranch on the eastern slope of the Rockies, one that began twenty years ago as a small-sized spread and grew slowly to medium size, where, possibly as much from deliberate choice as from the innate limitations of the owner, it has stayed.

It has been my purpose to present objectively modern ranching methods in such manner that the essential lore of the trade and the sequence of its jobs can be learned by the beginner. I have not, however, limited my material to the instructional, but have tried to show how ranch people look upon the life they have chosen, and what rewards and penalties it holds for them. I have tried, in other words, to follow the pattern of the hours on a ranch, and of the days and months, where work and contemplation and play follow each other like sunlight and shadow over a wind-swept butte.

I would perhaps not have embarked upon the task had I ever come across just the type of book that answers the questions that a man contemplating ranching as a career would ask. The literature of ranching seems to consist in two kinds —the romantic, also known as the "Westerns," and the pedagogic, written by the professional agriculturists. Neither wholly tells the story, for modern cattle ranching is not a continuing romance, nor is it entirely a cold-nosed business.

It is, for most of those who now follow it, a way of living as a family; it was thus with us, and I am thus presenting it, having uppermost in mind the legions of servicemen, now released or about to be released, who are confronted with the choice of a life career. A certain number of these men, in looking over the field, will come upon the idea of ranching. If for such men this book will serve to shorten the process of cut-and-try by which I, after the close of World War I, came to find a satisfying vocation, I shall feel well repaid for having sat indoors long enough to get it written.

# Contents

# THE
# *Compleat*
# RANCHER

# I. The Country

Cattle country is in general country that is too arid or too rough for the plow; it is, at this late date in the development of the West, land that does not interest the patient and ubiquitous farmer, land that, in the Indian's phrase, is still right side up. In such regions the natural grass cover is the only resource of value, and since this value is diffuse in nature, the works and habitations of man are far apart.

The area devoted to ranching is still vast and within it there is much diversity of soil, grass cover, water, and topography. To the beginner seeking a location, the vastness of the country may at first seem discouraging. Under the best of

3

conditions, with plenty of time and money at his command, he cannot hope to see more than a small fraction of the area of choice. Range country may be defined as that where cattle can graze out the greater part of the year. Its northern limit is on the banks of the Saskatchewan, and its southern on the Rio Grande. It extends from the 100th meridian on the east to the waters of the Pacific on the west.

If one is looking for a place to locate, and can afford to range widely, it is a good thing to do so. It is not, however, necessary to travel the length and breadth of the land to secure a wide range of choice. Cattle country has a third dimension which farming (and seafaring) lack—that of height. In many regions you do not have to travel far to see a lot of different range. Often, within less than a hundred miles, you can go from plains or desert into the low foothills, and from the low foothills into the high foothills, and into the mountain valleys and on to the mountain uplands. In all these types of country, except the last, one will find year-round locations where the ranch owner and his family are making a living that, by ranch standards, they deem adequate. Such ranches may be found on the arid outwash plains, or on the tablelands overlooking the lush irrigated valleys, or in the rolling, brush-covered foothills, or in the narrow valleys that finger into the high mountains, where the natural hay meadows are like green beads strung on the thread of the creek.

One will still encounter cattle outfits so big that they embrace all these different types of range. The number of such spreads is not, relatively speaking, large, and it is getting smaller all the time. It is not of this kind of ranching that I write, for it does not lie within my direct experience. These large ranches are those favored by the movie scenarists, with their great lowing herds, ample remudas of horses, a large low rambling house for the owner, and bunkhouses and line camps full of hard-riding, happy-go-lucky cowboys. Those which still carry on, amid the perplexities of ever-increasing land and labor costs, do not arouse the envy of their smaller neighbors.

Before going further I should perhaps define the family-sized ranch. It is one where the owner runs only the number of head that he himself can look after, where he has his critters under his eye at all times, where he works alongside his hired men, or trades work with the neighbors, and appears in person, instead of through a lawyer, at the meetings of the county board. In this type of ranching the association between staff and distaff side of the household is close and unquestioned; the hours of work are unprescribed, since work and rest are not sharply delimited, as where the man goes forth to an office in the morning and returns home in the afternoon. The ranch office is a corner of the living room; the possession of business sense by the owner, of the quick in-and-out variety, is not essential; the rewards are in part intangible, sometimes unanticipated, but, to those fitted by nature for the life, adequate.

As to size—which for a ranch is properly stated not in acres but in the number of head that can be run—the upper limit for this type seems to lie between five hundred and seven hundred and fifty head, and this is fixed not so much by the pasture available as by the number of menfolk that the missus with her daughters or hired girl can keep fed and bolstered and jollied up. The minimum size, that on which a fairly decent living can be made, is perhaps one hundred and fifty head; on this size the owner, with some traded work, can manage by himself. Between these limits the amount of summer range, of winter range, and of hay land will govern.

From this kind of ranch now come the great majority of the modern beef animals, blocky, well bred, well fleshed, to meet the standards of the present-day markets. The breeding and rearing of such cattle exacts close attention with careful treatment for the ever-increasing bovine pests and diseases. It means also the raising of ever-increasing quantities of hay and feed.

It is hard for the outfit running many thousands of head to give their critters this close attention, and to raise the feed. The profit in such ranching is now seldom great enough to hold much attraction for the investor, as such. His return is measured solely in cash; the owner-operator receives supplementary benefits—in self-sufficiency, in independence, in outdoor living. These intangible benefits hold him more surely to the land than do the dividend checks of the shareholder in the large commercial outfit, and therefore many of these outfits have broken up, or are cutting down their holdings. Those which survive enjoy extra favorable conditions or a superior kind of management.

This comment is by no means meant as a criticism of the big outfits, whose hospitality to me has upon many occasions been boundless; it is simply the statement of an economic law that seems to govern the cattle business. The force of this law is, oddly enough, the reverse of that now governing urban industry, where mergers and consolidations are the order of the day; in ranching this force seems rather to be centrifugal, with large units breaking up into smaller. The backwater thus created in the economic current affords, to the man who is so constituted that he wants to run his own show, an opportunity to do so.

But it is not enough to enter upon a ranching career solely from a desire for independence or from a dislike of city and suburb. These may help at certain unfavorable junctures, as when one gets both a heavy shrink and a falling price between gathering point and the railroad. The memory of past servitude or of past submergence in the crowds will wear off; there is a lot of hard work on a ranch.

One should have a direct and positive liking for the country; this is one attribute that all ranch people—north and south, east and west, large owners and small—have in common. There is thus one test available for your early use in determining whether you are cut out for ranching. It is whether you fit in with big, lonesome, silent, austere country.

If you find that such country lays a strong hand upon you, you can then proceed to apply some of the other tests, such as whether you have the physical equipment for the life, whether you can handle, or learn to handle, horses, and (for all but the most solitary in temperament) whether you have, or can find, a wife who also likes that kind of country.

Where you will eventually locate will be, after all, a matter of circumstance or, let us say, the result of fortune, birth, and predilection. Some one general region will be the area you favor above all others. You should bear in mind that within almost any range area there will be good, bad, and indifferent locations; you should certainly select a place that has at least a fair endowment of grass and water and the other attributes that make it possible to carry on. I shall give an outline of these attributes as the book develops. There are a few fool-proof regions where all land is equally good, like the Nebraska sandhills, but land comes high in such places and is parted with only under unusual circumstances.

The principal difference between ranching locations is that the higher up you are, or the farther north, the less your cattle can graze out and the more you have to feed them. The necessity of growing large amounts of feed, in the form of hay, or green feed, or small grains, will make the man in a high location into more of a farmer than his fellow on the low plains or desert, but in compensation, the thicker will be the grass cover, the clearer the water, and the better the scenery. A high location, in latitude or in elevation, demands not only greater labor in haying or harvest season but also more fencing, for pastures are smaller. But, as if to compensate for this extra labor, it seems to be a general rule that the higher, in latitude or altitude, that cattle are raised, the heavier they are at a given age, provided, of course, that they are well wintered. Thus, in our locataion, which lies between four and five thousand feet, and well toward the northerly limit of cattle country, our whiteface yearling steers average off grass in the fall about eight hundred pounds, and our yearling heifers about seven hundred and eighty-five pounds, and our calves at weaning four hundred and fifty pounds. These weights are about one hundred and fifty pounds heavier than those in the ranges of Arizona, New Mexico, and northern old Mexico with which I am familiar. I do not mean to imply by this that cattle raising up our way is necessarily more profitable than down south; the heavier weights are merely an attribute of our kind of country.

Even if it could be proved, as some of our friends have tried to do, that ranching in the Southwest is easier, we on our part would not want to make the shift. Once you have made your choice and get settled you are as reluctant to make a change as is a horse to leave the range where it was foaled. The Spanish have a word for that instinctive attachment, a word which ought to receive in ranching the stamp of current usage as much as those other Spanish works—lariat, cinch, and rodeo—which have become indispensable to the trade. This word is "querencia," meaning the place one likes, or the home range; it connotes the instinctive, sentimental attachment that has little to do with reason.

When, after a long search up and down the backbone of the continent, I dropped into our rolling brush-spotted foothills, I knew like the Mormons of old that this was the place. Most of my neighbors feel the same way about it. But not all do, for an unprosperous young neighbor of ours, born up here, did not flourish until he pulled stakes and located finally in a narrow valley of the Coast Range in central California, where the country greens up for two months of the year and the rest of the time the cattle, once they have finished the burr clover, have to eat a stiff and leached-looking grass that breaks under your tread. Yet I once rode through his cattle, standing with their eyes closed against the glare, and they had a thrift and a bloom that they never got when he ran his string up our way, where we are greened up five months and think that for the other seven there is no strength like the strength of our cured bunch grass. Verily the eye of the master fatteneth the cattle.

This man writes back to our country just twice a year, once when we are sweating to put up our hay in the heat of the summer and once when we are freezing to fork it out in the depth of the winter, times when we are liable to wonder whether the cattle are supporting us or we the cattle. Yet his range has pests such as screw worm and parasites and ticks that we never see, and I would rather work for a week haying, with the smell of fresh-cut timothy in my nostrils, than for a day at a dipping vat, where the terrified cattle have to be goaded into the steaming plunge, and come out stinking and half scalded.

This necessity of putting up a lot of hay we accept as part of the price we have to pay for our superior location, in the literal meaning of the term, and you must keep in mind, in your search for your own range, that the choice of a country that lies snowbound for part of the year exacts a far greater effort in putting up feed than a country not similarly handicapped. And haying is a chore, coming as it does in the hottest part of the year, when the flies bite hardest and men and horses tire easiest. Usually, too, the big rodeos and stampedes are held, for the tourists' benefit, spang in the middle of haying, when you have a crew on the job and can't get away. This looms large as a disadvantage when the radio blares forth its invitation, and the large multicolored posters appear in the town windows.

In compensation, however, there are around us a number of small local stampedes which come before haying, and these furnish a lot of fun. There is one each year about forty miles away, held with home talent in a natural amphitheater of the hills, where you sit on the banks and watch the events on the gravel flats below; these events include certain sports not seen at the big commercial events, such as Indian stake races. Our Blackfoot Indians are free to attend all stampedes, wherever held, for they have been wise enough not to encumber their lives with multitudinous possessions, such as cattle.

Putting up hay is not, however, a chore peculiar to snow-bound districts; all ranches must do it, and it is merely a matter of the quantity necessary. This universal task is obligatory because, in an average year, the market has come to demand animals of a certain type and conformation, and carrying good flesh. These conditions are seldom attained entirely on grass; at some age, at some time or other, your cattle must be fed. It has become standard practice all over range country to feed calves for a greater or lesser period, immediately after they are weaned. In southern districts this is about the only feeding done; in the north we have to have on hand enough hay to carry our cow herd through the winter storms. We carry separate winter pastures where the ungrazed grass is available when the snow does not cover it. This helps to reduce the amount of hay to be put up. Grass that lies beneath the snow in unavailable, since cattle are tropical in origin and in the thousands of generations since they were brought into northern climes the brutes have not learned to paw, as horses do, through the snow to the grass beneath. One, however, can view this shortcoming with less irascibility if one stops to think that mankind has also been slow to learn lessons of equal importance to its survival, such as that both sides lose in a war.

You will find in your search that this matter of balance between summer range and winter pasture is what usually sets the value of a ranch; too much of the one in proportion to the other throws the enterprise off balance. The predominance of the summer range over the winter operates to depreciate the value of a ranch; not so, however, the reverse. A deficiency of summer grazing can usually be made up more easily than one of wintering capacity. There will often be areas of public domain that one can get on, or one can join an association and share in their community pastures, or there is private pasturage for the renting from dried-out homesteaders, or sodbusters gone bust.

I should say, therefore, that in looking for a ranch, the safest rule is, after you have served, in order to learn the fundamentals, some kind of apprenticeship, either as a ranch hand or an unpaid volunteer, or even dead-heading on a dude outfit, to inquire diligently in the various districts you enter as to wintering questions, i.e., how much hay is required per head in an average season, and how many acres are necessary per head from first snow to greening up, and how much feed, as hay, or oat bundles, or sorghum, can be grown under average rainfall, or irrigation water. With these matters settled you can proceed to figure how many head you can carry through the tight or bottleneck season—whether it be the snowbound season in the north or the dried-up season in the south. In our country we find that we need a ton of hay—brome and timothy mixed—per head, and about five acres of grass, for safe and thrifty wintering. This is fairly high, but we get in compensation the heavy weights in the fall that I have referred to. We run a herd of all ages, from weaner calves through long yearling heifers and long two-year-old steers, together with the cows.

When you know the number you can winter you can then

proceed to match this, if possible, with summer grazing from greening up to first snow (or drying up). You can afford to take more of a chance on this end than on the wintering because you can always take in cattle for wintering on shares if you do not find at once your summer grazing. Or you can sell feed, which is available as an expedient to you as a beginner; the veteran cowman has such an antipathy to this procedure that he will usually let his hay rot in the field before he will sell it.

If your herd at the outset is too small to enlist your full time in the summer, you can work part time on wages. If you can get a riding job, for a bigger neighbor, or a stock association, or even the government, take that; if not, take a job setting fence posts or digging watering holes—anything to keep you in touch with ranching methods and procedures and ranching people, for ranching, in spite of the sparseness of the population in range country, has grown to be a community enterprise.

I shall have something more to say later about these two procedures, i.e., serving an apprenticeship and managing your herd. Since I am not writing a textbook but trying to set forth a way of life (which may be very congenial to some, but distasteful to others), I shall not attempt to treat any single aspect of ranch life exhaustively but rather to give the fundamentals of each so that the beginner can be guided in his choice, and once the choice is made, in his procedure. For the reader who wishes to go into the details of ranching I have listed in the Bibliography those books and pamphlets which I have found particularly useful.

Modern ranching on a small or medium scale is not, after all, a highly specialized, esoteric matter. You can forget nine-tenths of the western fiction that you have read. It requires some important fundamental knowledge, a fair amount of common sense, and after that a liking for the life. You, of course, can acquire by imitation as you go along some or all of the embroidering skills, the possession of which gives you increasing pride and efficiency. But if at first you can't rope a calf out of a gathered herd, you can drive the whole bunch into your corral, and there cut out the calves on foot and, after running them into a blind chute, grab them by the tails. If you can't rope and tie down an ailing critter in the pasture you can drive it in also, and put it in your chute, or if you prefer, and if you can't even rope it afoot, you can spread out one or two nooses in the corral dust and patiently wait until the critter steps into one of them. If you can't ride and manage a lifey horse, you can buy, or borrow, at the outset, a sturdy plug. Nine-tenths of handling cattle is done at a walk anyway —and ninety-nine one-hundredths should be. The gentler cattle are handled, the better; it is a matter of almost infinite patience. You should, I might add here, whether novice or to the manner born, start out with gentle well-bred foundation stock. It will be better to buy a few of this kind to start with than many of the half-wild type, that spook up easy, and at the sight of a horseman will tick off five miles and ten pounds of flesh at a lope; the kind that come in all colors, and all conformations—the ewe-necked, and cat-ham'd, the ridge-pole-back'd, the potbellied. This kind is fast disappearing, and as to the specimens that are left, it is better to leave them to the experienced cattleman who savvies their kind. You take the straight-run, bred-up kind, where the calves have been fed around the corrals or buildings their first winter, and handle easily.

And now, after these brief animadversions, let me get back upon the question of whether to go ranching at all, which of course is the first thing to be decided. I have proposed a test to determine whether you are cut out for the life, saying that the best touchstone is whether you like ranching country for itself. That question in the last analysis resolves itself into whether you have a measure of austerity in your soul. Range country is lonesome country, and you will be alone much of the time, whether you hire help or no, whether you are married or batch it. There is in ranching country a thinness of air, a sharpness of outline, and extremes of heat and cold. It lies quietly in the sunshine or starlight, or it is boisterous with wind, rain, or snow. There are no hazes, no mists; there is no mellowness. The range is etched into a myriad lines; it is bounded by an infinite horizon, or by stark mountains. It is big, and to use it for your cattle you must learn it, and there is little chance to learn it as you should unless you like it, for the learning process is long, and you should be buoyed up by just being alive and in it.

What you must learn about your range is, briefly: Where is the water, or where can water be developed? Cattle are lazy brutes and prefer to starve by a water hole rather than walk an hour to get into fresh grass. Where should the cattle be salted down so as to use the grass to the best advantage? Where can you find them at gathering time, be it an early cut for beef in the summer or the final roundup in the fall? Where do the predatory beasts roam? In some summer ranges, ours included, this is a governing consideration. Are there areas of poisonous weeds, and if so, are they the kind that are perennially poisonous, or merely seasonally? Are there soap holes, or bogs? And, if you own or lease your own summer range, how can you best run your fences so as to get the greatest advantage out of the wire for the least work?

You will learn in time to judge the country according to these and other standards, but only, I believe, if before that time comes you are living comfortably with the country. I recommend therefore that you find out alone with yourself as early as possible whether you are inwardly peaceful and happy in range country. It is certainly no reflection upon you if you come to find in the vast range country that East and West are hard to keep pushed apart.

If, however, you come to find a recurring sense of elation in being alive and in the country, you may have found your calling. This sense of elation is by no means continuous; you cannot expect it to be so. To run cattle exacts a lot of hard continuous work, and the greater part of the time you will be preoccupied with the job in hand. It is only at odd moments, days or even weeks apart, when you look up and see that the range, in whatever mood it may lie, in whatever aspect it may wear, is to your liking that you experience this lift of the spirit of which I speak.

It is profitless to analyze why this sense of elation comes over one. In my case I believe it is because range country, unscarred by the work of man, has perfection on a grand scale. It is as if some very choice work of art that one meets (but rarely meets) in a gallery should suddenly expand in its perfection to a scale as vast as all outdoors.

And it is silent country; there is too much noise in this mechanized world. Range country is quiet, and over it blows a clean, pure air. It is air that has not been breathed and burned and battle-smoked for untold generations.

## II. The Apprenticeship

It is, as I have said, desirable that you serve some kind of apprenticeship before you buy your land. The length and the arduousness of this will vary with your prior experience and your wealth, but there is no substitute for doing most of the ranch jobs yourself. Both prior experience and coin in your purse may shorten the period, but should not be invoked to eliminate it. The man is fortunate who has some farming experience in his background, even if it is not his own, but in the nature of family lore, acquired perhaps from a parent or a grandparent who in the healthy interchange of population that used to prevail between farm and city had exchanged a

19

rural for an urban way of life. Ranching is but a larger kind of animal husbandry.

If you have at the outset enough capital to buy some land and a herd, you may use this advantage to shorten your apprenticeship, but you should not forgo it. You may perhaps limit it to the more elementary lessons, and then proceed with a good hired hand. The selection, however, of such a man in itself demands experience in judging whether a job is well done, and in learning what is the measure of a good day's work. There is a distinct limit to the rate at which you can spend money in developing a ranch. Under the best conditions this spending, once you have a shelter over your head and the nucleus of a herd, should be interrupted for protracted periods if you are to learn by making your mistakes on a small scale.

The West is full of what the cattleman calls "blueprint ranches" where the owner has started out with more capital than judgment, and has spread corrals, shelter sheds, and buildings all over the lot. This type of spending usually betokens an unwillingness on the part of the boss to get out and work himself. Fortunately for the appearance of the country, the hot sun and the hard winds soon weather these structures down to where they fit into the landscape, and the owner thereof either comes to fit into the ways of the country or some hard-bitten and laconic neighbor gets his land on an easy lease.

An apprenticeship is useful both to learn how to do the

various jobs and also what attitude to take toward the life. The latter is the more important of the two. If you come from a world of ringing telephones, scribbled memos, and pep meetings, you may find at first that the pace of life is intolerably slow. The first lesson, therefore, is to learn to fall into the tempo of country living, wherein the hours between dawn and dark are not to be divided into the daily stint and recuperation therefrom, but constitute an indivisible unit of living time, work and recreation being alike in complexion.

It takes some little time for the city dweller to learn that ranching (or farming, for that matter) is a way of life to be followed, and not a job to be held down. Take, for example, the slowest paced job in all ranching, that of trailing cattle. A well-handled drive travels about two miles an hour— slower if the herd consists of cows and calves. If the cattle are well handled they seem to flow along the trail rather than walk, and flow at the rate of cold molasses. The tedium of a drive of ten hours or more a day used to seem unendurable when I first went into ranching. We have a drive, which we make each fall, between our summer range on a national park and the flat irrigated country, where the steers are grain-finished for market. It is a distance of about one hundred miles, and lies for the greater part across an immense bald Indian reservation, where there is scarcely a house, a fence, or a tree. When I first took that drive, years ago, it was absolute, unadultered boredom—a four-day ordeal.

I have just returned from it as I write these words. The

same four days went by so quickly and pleasantly that I was sorry to see, shimmering on the far horizon, the dark line of the cottonwoods that marked the borders of the farm country. The difference? I have merely learned to use the time to advantage, as do my cowpuncher companions. I studied the herd and picked out the individual animals that I had thrown out on the range six months before, at the beginning of summer. I noted how the individuals had fleshed up; some uniformly with an even coating of fat over their ribs and loins so that they looked as if they had been carved out of a cake of soap. These would be the tops of the herd. Then there were others which, on the same grass, had put their fat on in patches, at the tail head or on the flanks, and others which had run to potbellies. On both of these classes the packer buyers would strive hard for a cut in price. A fortune awaits the purebred man who can furnish foundation stock that fleshes up uniformly. This matter lies in the realm of animal genetics, of which more later.

To be able now to pick out the individual critters I had on a previous drive memorized them; this took time then, for our herd is of Hereford breeding, a breed that seems to the newcomer uniform to the point of dreariness. But study will serve to differentiate them; my method is to memorize the patterns of red and white about the necks of the individuals. It is a useful faculty to acquire; you can thus keep track of individual progress on feed ground or summer range, and on the latter you can tell what is missing from the gather.

Then I had used the time to work with my horse, an intelligent, willing, but green four-year-old gelding. Young or old, there is seldom a cow horse so good that it cannot stand a little more schooling. If he is clumsy about turning, you can work on that—a cow pony should turn on his hind feet. If he is spooky about something, such as a rope dragged across his haunches, or a paper lunch bag, you can work on that. You can get out your rope, and dab a loop on a fence post or buck brush, or if you are pretty good at it, over the rump of a critter. Or, dropping behind for a moment, you can teach your horse to walk up, for a good fast walk is perhaps the single most valuable attribute of a cow horse.

I had acquired, since coming into the country, an interest in grasses, and I strove to identify, as I walked along leading my horse, some of the thirty-odd palatable varieties that the agrostologists tell us grow on our ranges. We passed many areas where the huge horse herds of the Indians had grazed these grasses to the roots, and it was interesting to see the effects of erosion on such portions of the range—how the rains runneled the cattle trails and gopher colonies. There are in different countries different criteria of overgrazing. For our country the scientists at the Range Experiment Station have picked out a low-lying bluish lichen called Selaginella, and although they haven't been able to get us to call it by name, have taught us to be on the watch for it.

Another indication of overgrazing is the color of the pastures in the spring of the year, at greening-up time. As you ride through a country of checkerboard pastures you will notice that some are greener than others, which means that these green ones have been overgrazed either fall or winter; gone is the old grass that by its brown color masks the green of the new. New grass is "washy," and scours the cattle if taken alone; therefore, each mouthful the critter gets should include some of the old hard grass of the previous season.

There was some night riding on this last trip—there is, first and last, a good deal of such on a ranch. It can be tedious too; the remedy for me is to study the stars, and here is where the man from the city may have some advantage over the men born on the range, in that he knows that there are simple and ingenious star finders to be bought. The cowman, like all pastoral folk from David onward, is impressed by the stars:

> Last night as I rode on the prairie
> And gazed at the stars in the sky,
> I wondered if ever a cowboy
> Could go to that sweet bye and bye.

Few cattlemen, however, know much about the stars, and if you can furnish them with some information it will be gratefully received.

✿

Thus I have, by the use of these and similar devices, learned to banish tedium from one ranching job, that of trailing cattle.

I do not mean to claim priggishly that I put all my time on a drive to work in such profitable manner; a lot of it passes unmarked, in long languorous hours when the horse's head goes down and his ears swivel lazily, while with a mind innocent of care or thought I watch the dust devils whirling below and the heat mirages over the plains, and above, floating like clouds, the white crests of the peaks.

And I always ride a good horse; in any activity on a ranch that involves the joint effort of a horse and rider, monotony cannot really take much of a hold—like a well-founded marriage, the association in itself precludes it.

But in the type of ranching I am describing the proportion of time you spend in the saddle is not so extensive as you would judge from reading western stories. I suppose that on our place we average the year around one-quarter of our working hours on horseback. Spring and fall there are times when one rides nearly all the time; summer and winter but little, for in winter feeding and chores take up the greater part of the time; in summer fencing and haying.

The latter are two jobs that are plain hard work; there is a lot of them on a family-sized ranch, and, if you are properly to appraise the career, you should include them in your apprenticeship. Here physical exertion precludes mental diversions; there may be people whose minds can function well and smoothly when they are engaged in hard physical work, but I am not among them.

The way to do both these jobs is to make up your mind that

they have to be done, and start in the morning at a pace that you can pretty well sustain all day, and don't look ahead too far; this piece of advice was once given me in a form that made it stick. When I first started in ranching I was given a job of fencing; this involved digging a mile of post holes, each a rod apart, and therefore three hundred and twenty to the course. With each shovelful of dirt that thought oppressed me; I could see, marching ahead of me over hill and dale, the interminable pickets that marked the mile. I groaned audibly at the prospect, and my partner working with me heard it. He had been long in the country.

"Son," he said, "the trouble with you is that when you are digging one post hole you are digging all the others too. Try digging them one at a time."

There is another attribute to fencing that makes it a good tryout job for the life of a rancher. This is the handling of barbed wire—of all modern inventions the most nefarious. In itself it is snaky, malevolent, treacherous; in its effects it has ruined countless thousands of horses; it has broken up many a proud cattle spread; it has degraded the ancient and once honorable art of war. It never misses a chance to spring out at the unwary handler; it tears his clothing and lacerates his flesh. And yet but for its invention your small ranch would never have been possible; nor would prairie farming—in fact, the tilling of fields in this country would have been limited to those areas where there were stones to be laboriously amassed or rails to be split out from trees.

A word of caution here lest your inexperience, coupled perhaps with a creditable humanitarian impulse, lead you into the error of two neighbors of mine. They were brothers, and came new to the country from Denmark where they had learned the animal husbandry of that thrifty and kindly land.

They proceeded to take up quarter-section homesteads, which they fenced with *smooth* wire. Their cattle were western and paid no attention to this, although the fence was four-wire and strung tightly; the animals came and went about as they pleased—into their neighbors' hayfields, up onto the brushy mountainsides, and across the rivers and far away. The smooth wire proved absolutely ineffective. The brothers were constrained to do all their fencing over again.

There is, of course, one use to which smooth wire can advantageously be put and that is for fencing a pasture to be used exclusively for horses. One of the most frequent sorrows that any rancher has is to find some horse suffering from a barbed-wire cut. One is, however, seldom set up so that he can devote one pasture exclusively to horses, and, if he is, then he must expect to see, without anger, a fair proportion of his neighbors' cattle therein.

The exertion and difficulties of fencing are rewarded like all such ranch jobs by final satisfaction. When you have finished you can look down a taut straight line, properly braced and four-square at the corners, running between you and your neighbors. And out west, as in old New England, it is still the truest of the true that "good fences make good neighbors."

✿

The other dismounted chore that I recommend for your apprenticeship is, as I have said, haying. Unlike fencing, which can be fitted into other work, and, to be candid, can be fudged a little by interspersing other tasks, haying once started must be pursued relentlessly to the end. Hay has a certain stage of maturity when it is at its best. With alfalfa this occurs when it is about one-third blossomed out; with timothy and brome, just after blooming. Then you have to be all organized to go, with your machinery—mowers, rakes, and stacker—all set to go, your teams caught up, feet trimmed, and gentled down.

Haying means long hours on the pitching, tossing, ironclad seat of a mower, or on a rake, or on the deck of a rack, or, most strenuous of all, on the top of the stack, where the hay comes rolling up inexorably, like the breakers of a flood tide.

The weather is hot, the flies are out, your companions, born to the life, intolerant of delay. Here is straight and sustained physical work; it can be disheartening if you start in too soft of body. If, however, you are in some kind of condition at the outset, it is amazing how your body will respond to the demand upon it when it is put to the kind of work for which untold generations before the advent of the machine age have conditioned it. In haying, unlike fencing, there is a sustaining force in the nature of the material you are handling, which is sweet smelling and but one stage removed from good roast beef—or surging horsepower, in the literal meaning of the term. And haying is the epitome of thrift, and as you work you may be able to picture to yourself the white drifts of winter, the driving storms from the north, and the cattle standing around on the feed grounds contentedly munching away at your good green hay and keeping thrifty and warm. It is a great feeling in the fall of the year, when the first storm comes, to look out over your meadows and see the neat stacks waiting each in its appointed place.

If you have some grain land—and in time you invariably come to have such—you have another job kindred to haying, that is, harvesting. This is usually brisk but short, and also aided by the buoyancy felt in reaping that which you have sown. There are other jobs throughout the year which can become monotonous if they stretch out, as they do once in a while. Among these are cutting your stovewood (if you live in the foothills) or hauling gravel for your corrals, or hoeing up your garden. All these, however, have an element of interest, and with the changing seasons the cattle change in their needs, and it all adds together to as little monotony and as much solid enjoyment as any trade with which I happen to be familiar.

In the periods of monotony that do occur you may, however, if you come from the city, have an advantage over the people born to the life—you may be able to draw from a previous existence the comfort that elsewhere there is monotony too. About the toughest hour of the day in haying comes at five in the afternoon; I can tell myself that at that hour in a previous incarnation I used to be hanging on a subway strap.

✿

An apprenticeship in its broad aspect has also this useful purpose: you get in with the ways of the people. Small- or medium-scale ranching is, in spite of the distances separating neighbors, an interdependent affair. Certain of the jobs can be done expeditiously only when a crew is on hand. You will thus want to trade labor with your neighbors at branding time, at harvest time, and at roundup time.

You may also want at certain times to trade for special skills of one sort or another. It is surprising how many diverse accomplishments can be found within riding distance in the average ranching country. One neighbor may have had veterinary training, another may have been a blacksmith, another perhaps knows fine carpentry, another may have acquired a knowledge of tractor mechanics. Even the strangest skills are sometimes available. For instance, in our country there was at one time an intensive exploration for oil—fortunately for our peace of mind unsuccessful. The drillers, in changing cables, left on the ground when they pulled out many short lengths of wire rope. These are extremely useful in various ranch structures, particularly in fencing across our numerous rivers, but they were no good in short lengths. It developed that an old homesteader, up in the brush, had at one time been a cable splicer, which is a skilled trade. He became one of the most popular men of the district.

The various skills of which I speak are traded back and forth without too exact a balancing of the accounts.

In our family we even once traded for music lessons for the children by a kind of two-cushion shot—the loan of a tractor to the son-in-law of a talented woman. In fact, the only trade I know of for which there would be no demand would be that of income tax accounting. Ranchers seldom have need for that kind of thing, and in the occasional years when they do they do not want to be reminded of the fact.

Oddly enough you not infrequently can get labor on a trade when you cannot for cash. I do not know why this is unless because the value of labor varies enormously with its timeliness, as in haying or gathering beef.

It confers therefore a great advantage on a newcomer to bring in some kind of skill for which there is a demand. It would well repay a man contemplating a ranching career to acquire some such special skill, say in a night trade school.

I had fortunately two of these to offer—welding and surveying. I keep a welding outfit in my blacksmith shop, which in such busy times as haying is invaluable for quick repairs, for example when a neighbor has "broken down" in this crowded season. This term, by the way, has nothing to do with a mental or physical collapse, but means simply that the

implement which is then in seasonal use has failed mechanically. There is also an occasional call for my services as a
levelman in surveying irrigation ditches, or in laying out a
stock-watering dam.

The independent spirit of ranching people is such that a
service is seldom requested unless there is the willingness and
the ability to return it. This willingness is implied rather than
expressed, for the typical cattleman is chary of much in the
way of promise, or even of conversation.

All the complex relationship of neighbors is, in fact, governed by an unwritten code—you might even say by unwritten
punctilio—and it is well for the newcomer to learn the principal tenets of this code. Thus you are expected to maintain
one-half the length of a fence that divides you from your
neighbor. You will never be reminded of that fact, but the
atmosphere will grow chilly if you do not do so. You are
expected to give the other fellow notice for the first time, and
again the second, when his stray stock gets into your pasture;
the third time you can throw it out on the nearest commons,
or impound it, or do anything short of appropriating it.

You should also know such items as that the same man
who in selling you cattle will scrupulously point out any defects, down to a spoiled teat, would, if he could, foist upon
you a blind horse, and that you cannot ask a man how many
head of cattle he owns without risk of giving offense; it is
like asking a city man how much money he has in the bank.

All these things conjoin, as I set out to show at the beginning of this chapter, to make it advisable for the newcomer in ranching country to serve an apprenticeship of longer or shorter duration. I came to this country with a little money jingling in my pockets from the sale of some mining claims, and though I served for a while, I did not serve long enough. I made three mistakes the first season. I got stove up by persisting in riding a horse that was a jughead—and showed it; I nearly lost the friendship of a neighbor by fencing in a trail that had run through my land since Indian days; and I ran out of hay the first winter because I had been too busy that summer fishing in the river that bordered my property. But I caught an eight-pound cutthroat trout, and looking back now I remember more of the thrill of pulling out that fish than the distress of freighting in hay from a distance.

## III.  The Critter

Y ou will not be long in range country before hearing the maxim: "First look after your cattle, then after your horse, and then after yourself." This consideration for the critter is strange in that it seldom has in it any element of affection; I have never known of a cattleman who, when the proper time had come to sell off his cattle, has parted with them with any other feeling than pleasure—except perhaps when adversity of one kind or another had forced him to sell young breeding stock.

Paradoxically, when for some reason he comes to sell a saddle horse, he may really grieve over the parting, although he would risk the neck of that horse—and his own—not once but many times when the business demands it, as when, on the fall roundup, he sees some stray way down a mountain trail greasy with wet snow.

Perhaps this peculiar attitude comes from the fact that the cow stands in a unique relationship to the business. She is at

once a capital item and an item of merchandise. In her youth
and maturity she is a producing unit; in her old age she
becomes, after a preliminary fattening period, a piece of merchandise on the shelf awaiting sale. I know of no other business where this circumstance is duplicated.

All your hope of reward thus centers about her; without her
all your grass, all your hay, and all your fences become worthless. Pride and profit and a long tradition all demand that you
take all possible care of your cattle, from the time the calf
gets up on its wobbly legs until the car doors slam upon it as
it goes to the stockyards. Let us therefore proceed to some of
the lore of the trade.

Calves should preferably be dropped just about, or a little
before, the time that the grass greens up. On southern ranges,
this will be about the time that the rains are scheduled to
begin; in our northern country, when the snow, except for the
lingering drifts, has gone. By that time you should have your
cow herd close in, and be riding regularly through it, looking
for calving sign. On our northern ranges, where the coat is
still shaggy at this time, the girth of the cow is not so good
an indication as the state of the udder. A cow begins to
"make bag," that is, her udder begins to swell, shortly before
she calves. Parenthetically, you must learn to read a cow's
udder before you can call yourself much of a stockman. The
cow's udder is your business index, the wallboard graph
which the progressive businessman keeps always posted to
date. It shows the past and present condition of that particular

producing unit—whether she has ever had a calf, whether she is going to have a calf, whether she now has a calf, and if so, what kind of matron she is.

When you see her making bag, then you watch for a swelling of the vulva; when this occurs her time is near. If the weather is good, and the cow is thrifty, it is best to leave her on clean pasture; otherwise you may want to throw her into a near-by corral, which should not be wet or muddy, for closer observation. Calves are born normally with forefeet and head coming first and with but little trouble. It is, however, well for the owner to familiarize himself with the various forms of false presentation that occur. Heifers calving for the first time are especially subject to such. The dam should not be allowed to linger too long in labor, but be given help by manipulating the calf; the amount of force to be applied is a matter of common sense, and the direction of that force limited to getting the head and forefeet to come first. The need for this kind of help is infrequent; in our herd, which is about ten per cent replacement heifers, not in more than two per cent of the cases.

The period of gestation in cattle is about the same as in human beings; the ratio of twin to single births is, oddly enough, about the same. Fortunately, with these two items the resemblance between bovine and human multiplication ceases; the cow, when, in the Spanish phrase, about to give to the light, loses her gregarious instinct and seeks solitude, as in a clump of brush or in a coulee bottom. This innate trait no doubt proceeds from a desire to conceal her young and helpless calf. The human mother seems to develop at such times an even stronger gregariousness, and proceeds to the best and largest hospital available, where, shortly after the event, she holds an at-home, and the baby is put on exhibition behind glass.

This tendency to hide away at calving time makes it imperative for the stockman to ride long hours, not only to help out in difficult parturitions, which, as I have said, are fortunately rare, but more importantly, to extricate a calf dropped in a tangle of brush, or head down a steep bank, or at the margin of a stream or lake. The rider does well to have a number of gunnysacks tied to his cantle, wherewith to rub dry a new calf if it should come in a rain squall or a snow flurry. Incidentally, when handling a new calf, it is well to keep an eye on the dam, lest your attentions be misinterpreted. The hardihood of new calves is nothing short of amazing, and in many years has never ceased to evoke my wonder and gratitude. Our spring storms are fairly frequent at calving time, and of the calves born therein the vast majority survive, even when near-blizzard conditions prevail.

Once a calf has got to its feet and had its first drink of warm milk, its career is safely launched. The cow licks it over carefully, her eyes assume that glazed air of pride which is the utmost refinement of bovine complacency, and she leads her calf back to the herd, where within a few days it is butting at butterflies, and hightailing it in youthful exuberance. This herd, at this time, should consist only of calvy females. Steers and dry she-stuff should have been cut away from this herd before calving time. I should explain that by the term "dry" is meant any female that does not show signs of calving or that does not have a calf. Steers are insatiably curious and bother the new calves; the dry cow sometimes has a stronger maternal instinct than her more favored sister, and, left in the same pasture, may try to rob her of her calf.

When riding through your herd at calving time use your quietest horse and leave any dog or visitors from the city behind. I make it a practice at such times to take a quick glance at any new calf; if its eye is bright and its coat shows a cowlick or two, I ride by as if the matter did not interest me, which the cow prefers to see. I, however, mark the spot, and keep an eye out to see whether the cow sooner or later leads forth her progeny. Once it is sucking, you can chalk up another one of those basic ranch producing units known as a cow-and-calf-at-foot. The most significant index of your success on a ranch is the percentage of annual calf crop; this is the number of calves dropped divided by the number of females exposed to the bulls the previous summer. This percentage figure is generally higher for the small or medium-sized ranch than for the larger, since in the former class breeding pastures are generally smaller, water holes more frequent or better developed, and more riding to distribute the bulls is done. Bulls tend to gang up as the breeding season goes along, and such gentlemen's clubs defeat the purpose of the owner. On our place this calf crop percentage varies from eighty to ninety, with an average of about eighty-five.

As a rule the milk supply of the cow and the demands of her calf are pretty well matched, especially if the calves come before the grass is too lush (which makes for a large milk flow). But some cows will have too much milk anyway, and you will have to drive them into the corrals, put them on dry feed, and probably, to save one or more quarters of their udders from spoiling, milk them out by hand. You will put the cow in your chute, which should be provided with a drop-board on one side, catch her head, and proceed as best you can. This is a nasty little chore, and results not infrequently in a sprained thumb, for she resents the attempt at relief. Fortunately the growing calf and the diminishing milk flow tend to make this a short chore.

In all cow herds there are some of the basic cow-and-calf units that come apart; that is, the cow dies, or her milk flow ceases, or the calf dies. Also when a cow has twins, she usually plays gross favorites, cherishing the first-born and kicking off the second. Then the stockman plays that simple but tedious form of range dominoes, known as "matching up." You drive in a calfless cow and rope up an orphan calf. You then try to persuade the indignant cow that the loss of her own was but a bad dream. The calf, which is not particular, can usually be depended upon to carry out the deceit by butting the cow's udder and making appealing ba-a-ah's. In time, the cow may accept the convention, and after she has nourished the calf a few days becomes again the usual zealous matron. The process is easier if you have a pen or box stall, and do not have to use an open corral.

A sure way for the recalcitrant cow, if natural association fails, is to find and skin out the dead calf of the cow, and drape this skin over the orphan calf. Cows—and most animal dams—claim their young by the sense of smell. Possibly you, in contemplation of such a thing, and the kindred chores of veterinary work and home butchering, may find yourself a bit squeamish; that should not deter you from ranching as there are very few cases where squeamishness in war or in ranching survives the test of going up against realities.

It is seldom that you can exactly match up all bereaved cows and orphaned calves; it is well therefore to have on hand at calving time an extra fresh milk cow or two, so that you can pail-raise your orphans. It is not hard to teach a calf to drink from a pail if, when it is hungry, you dip your fingers in the milk and let the calf suck them. In a few weeks you can change the calf over from whole milk to skim milk, supplemented perhaps by some store calf meal. It is not desirable to skim-milk a calf—an experienced cattleman can spot such an animal three years later—but it is better than losing the calf.

Calving time should last about the length of time of the association of the bulls and cows the previous summer. This period we like to restrict to one hundred and twenty days. To leave the bulls in too long results in a few late calves that had better never been born; they cannot be weaned with the rest in the fall, and they spoil the uniformity of the bunch, which counts a great deal in the market pens. Four months of exposure of your cow herd will comprise at least four breeding periods of the cow, which comes in heat every three weeks.

Calving season usually opens up with a rush, and then tapers off, which is fortunate, as the other spring jobs then become insistent. Most ranchers who have gathered their cow herds close in for calving will, in order to save close-in pastures—usually the smallest in area—make periodic gathers of the strong matrons and their calves, and push these finished jobs out to a larger pasture, or, if not too distant, to the permanent summer pasture. This makes it easier to look after the remainder.

The cows and calves on their summer range form the pleasantest sight of all to the rancher's eye—unless perhaps, for the more practical minded, it is surpassed by a drove of fat steers heading for the railway in the fall. I take endless satisfaction in the summer scene, with the calves gathered in a nursery under the supervision of the matron-of-the-day, the cows grazing away on the green grass, a warm sun overhead, and the good green grass underfoot. That is the way the western country should be used; the stockman and the Indian, at variance on many points, at least agree on this: that the plow turns the land wrong side up.

✿

As in the human race, the outcome of the calf depends not alone on the kind of care it gets, but also on its ancestry. It is therefore of the utmost importance that you start with the right kind of foundation cows, and breed them to the right kind of bulls. A poor start takes generations of breeding to remedy; it is far better to buy fewer matrons, but have them right.

Judging cattle is not a science, but an art; it is the cumulative effect of many details that produce the finished effect, and one can easily go astray in getting preoccupied with the details and forgetting the over-all impression. Thus, the score cards that are furnished by many breed associations are more bewildering than helpful to the average beginner. Head, neck, shoulders, girth, flank, quarters and hams—all have a part in the complete picture; none can be out of scale or depart far from the norm, but no single one can be emphasized to the exclusion of the others. All give clues to the thrift and productivity of the individual, to its capacity to turn grass into salable pounds. Yet it is not the over-all gain in weight alone that determines value, for the weight must be put on in the right places, that is, where the most valuable cuts are.

It is well for the beginner, in making his choice of females, to enlist the services of some experienced man. In every range country there are itinerant cattle buyers, and it is worth paying such a man a commission on the selection of the first purchase.

I would recommend, for the foundation stock, that one lean toward scale and size, even if with this one has to accept some departure from the ideal of smoothness. Refinement of conformation can come with time, by the use of smooth bulls.

There has been in the past ten years too much emphasis placed on smoothness as contrasted with scale; this has been because the demand has been for cuts for the delicatessen trade, small in size. The animal that will flesh up earliest, under heavy feed in the farmer's barnyard, produces these cuts. The process of forcing a calf or a light yearling to early maturity by means of crowding it with grain is an uneconomical way of producing beef. Such baby beef is also less appealing to the practiced palate than mature beef. An animal should be carried along to a respectable weight, somewhere around one thousand pounds on good outdoor grass, and then perhaps given the finishing touches in the feed lot. This is the economical way to turn out pounds of beef, and, if the practice is reverted to, the cost of beef, which has trended at times toward the prohibitive, will come down to where working people can afford to purchase. That section of the market which demands small and extremely fat carcasses the rancher can well leave to the farmer-grower of beef cattle, who lives close in to the big cities.

The protracted feeding of light animals on expensive grains which could better be used for processing into food or into industrial products may in the postwar world prove to be a luxury that a hungry world cannot afford. It takes from six to ten pounds of grain, plus roughage, to make a pound of highly finished beef, and this amount of grain could better be made into direct foods, or countless industrial chemicals.

Grass in the great range areas can, on the other hand, be put to only one use, which is to make meat, or—to contemplate for a moment a distasteful subject—wool.

On grass alone, either green or cured into hay, you will get satisfactory weights if you have chosen the right kind of cows and have bred them to the right kind of bulls. You will get these bulls from the purebred man, and this is perhaps the place to say something about the purebred business, with which, in one way or another, you will always be in contact. I should like to start out, as a range cattleman, by paying tribute to the breeder of registered stock. I can perhaps best do it by going back to the early days of the cattle business, to compare the weight of the steer that came up over the Chisholm Trail and that of the steer you will now find in countless western pastures. Then, barely fifteen cattle generations ago, the earliest age at which a steer was deemed fit to gather for beef was four years—and better at five. He would then weigh around one thousand pounds, and much of that thousand would be tough and stringy, being located on neck and shoulders and brisket. The modern packer-buyer would cut the best of his kind down to common grade, calling him (with embellishments) long-legged, cat-ham'd swaybacked, and high in the tail head. This steer to boot was about as wild as a buffalo and it took a real cowpuncher to handle him.

Now, on good range, a thousand-pound animal is produced as a long two, i.e., at the age of two years and some months. He is blocky, evenly fleshed, docile; his dressing percentage, off grass, is from fifty-five to fifty-eight; much of his weight is in the choicer cuts that bring the money.

On his dam's side he is a direct descendant of the wild range cow of the seventies and eighties.

This vast improvement has come almost entirely from the use of purebred bulls. And these, with one unimportant exception,* have come from the beef breeds of the British Isles: they are the Durham (Shorthorn), the Angus, the Galloway, and the Hereford. Thus my tribute must extend not only to the purebred men on this continent, but to their predecessors overseas.

You may throw out of the reckoning, if you are so disposed, all our other debts to the British people, from Magna Carta to the Blitz of 1940, but you will still owe them a heavy debt on this count alone. It was the importation of purebred herds from Great Britain that accomplished the transformation of the Spanish-type cattle into the modern beef critter. We have, to be sure, achieved much refinement in the successive generations, but the duration of the refining process has been short compared to the length of upbreeding at their hands. In these English and Scots breeds—bovine, equine, and ovine—we had ready to hand a bonanza—refined germ plasm—greater in worth than all the glamorous bonanzas of the early West—the Comstock Lode, Butte des Morts, Bingham Canyon, Goldfield, Bisbee. When you go

---

* The Brahma, which on the tick-infested ranges of the extreme south, is crossed into the standard beef breeds.

about selecting your bulls, you will do well to keep in mind the gaitered English squire, the yeoman in homespun, the braw Scots herdsmen.

✿

This selection of your bulls, spring or fall, is the legitimate excuse for those trips away from your ranch without which the best man can go stale—those trips to see, and learn, and to relax. The purebred men have their establishments scattered over all the range areas of the West; they tend to group near the towns, for greater accessibility, and near the farming areas, the better to grow or to buy feed. In time you will come to know the established purebred men who, in that exacting trade, have won through to a firm reputation.

You can purchase their product at private treaty at the ranch or at the public auction sales to which they consign a fair share of their output. They are on the whole a reliable group, possessing in extreme degree the quality of patience; they can be depended upon for good counsel, although perhaps not always quick to point out the defects that may be hidden by the heavy covering of flesh their ready-to-market animals are carrying.

My choice in buying is to get bulls at the ranches; one has there somewhat more time to look at the quality of the herd, and one sees the dams from which the bulls spring. You can usually buy them a little cheaper at the ranch, since the breeder is not put to the expenses of an auction; there is also the natural combativeness of the human species, and pride of opinion often gets involved in bidding, and livestock auctioneers are adept in scenting out rivalries at the ringside.

You, however, may well come to the conclusion that you are justified in paying slightly higher prices at the auction sales. You will have thrown in a sociable time with your fellow cattlemen, coming as they do from a wide area, expansive in a jovial, city-visiting mood. Your womenfolk will, as like as not, be along, and they will catch the enthusiasm of the crowd and find out at first hand some of the elements of the business, which they otherwise must get, I am afraid, only in preoccupied monosyllables around the kitchen table.

Incidentally, the judging of livestock being, as I have said, an art, the gentler sex in this, as in all matters involving artistic perception, quite often develop a surprising degree of skill, as witness the number of girls who win 4-H Club championships, and make their college livestock judging teams.

Purebred breeding can become a very seductive branch of animal husbandry, and it takes considerable fortitude to attend sales year after year without launching into the business by the purchase of a few cows or heifers. There is always the vision before you of finding in your pasture one morning a future Denver, or Calgary, or Chicago International winner. As one who has not been wholly successful in resisting the impulse I cannot consistently proclaim that the commercial

cattleman should not mix into the purebred game; I can, however, counsel that he defer his entry until such time as he
has acquired a good eye for cattle and a purse deep enough
to sustain the early expense.

As one travels about in the selection of bulls, one should
carry a mental image of his own cow herd, and endeavor to
select males with complementary qualities. If your cows tend
toward the big and rough, select smooth bulls; if they are
smallish and fine boned, select rugged and sizable ones. If
they are high off the ground, take low bulls, and so on.
When you find a bull, or bulls, that you want, remember
that there is such a thing as being penny wise and pound
foolish in this as in all other businesses. Your bulls are half
the herd, although in numbers perhaps not more than five
per cent. The leverage that a good bull can exert upon herd
improvement is thus enormous.

I would advise the beginner to buy at the outset only two-
year-old bulls, which is the beginning of their serviceable
career. Later, when you become a good judge of cattle, you
can, if there seems to be economy in the process, buy yearlings.
To buy bull calves is, to my notion, to take on too much of a
gamble, in a business that has too much, as it is, of the element of chance; it is very difficult, even for an old hand, to
see in the calf the mature animal.

One final caution: beware the bull that has been fitted to
show condition by such a farfetched method as the use of a
nurse cow. This is, to my mind, a reprehensible error into

which, under the urge of winning show-ring honors, too many
of our purebred men are falling. By this is meant the keeping
of a bull calf on a nurse cow after separation from its dam
at the natural weaning time. If persisted in, the practice will
obscure the natural milking qualities of the breed and mask
the fleshing qualities. A bull should be fitted on natural commercial feeds—grain and hay—or not at all. The Hereford
men are especially prone to this practice.

A bull of the beef breeds becomes serviceable at two years
of age. To use him earlier is to run the risk of stunting him,
and spoiling him. You can use him in your herd until he is
five years old, at which time his first crop of heifers comes
of breeding age, that is, at two years. You can use him longer
if you cut away from his harem the heifers which are, or may
be, his daughters. You can breed these to unrelated bulls.
It is poor practice to keep a bull on the job too long; we
never use one that is over six years of age, and then only if
he is thrifty and snorty. Beyond that age, a bull is apt to get
logy, and lose his youthful zest; he is inclined to become
heavy, like the Turk in a cartoon, and footsore, and to hang
around a few favorites near a water hole. At five or six years
of age he is generally in good flesh, and will bring a fair
price on the block, for what is known as the bologna trade.
His value then is generally from one-quarter to one-third of
what you paid for him, so in buying him you should have
in mind this salvage value.

Purebred bulls generally handle easily; you do not have to

worry as in the dairy breeds about their becoming dangerous. In all my experience with beef bulls I have known only two that have shown signs of a desire to attack a man. In beef breeds it is the cow that you want to keep your eye on.

# IV. The Critter

### (*Continued*)

Next, when calving is oe'r, men's whole thought goes to the
offspring
And they stamp them anon with brands distinguishing each one
As preference dictates: these for maintaining a true breed,
These for sacred office, and these as laboring oxen
Upturning the rugged loam-clods, and straining across them,
While the others at grass go forth as an army to pasture.

Book III—The Georgics (Brodribb's Translation) *

Thus it was in Virgil's day (although you will find many
writers on ranching crediting the Spanish colonists with
the invention of the branding iron) and thus it is in our day.
Thus it will always be, unless the geneticists ultimately find
some way (more reliable than Jacob's) of marking the calves
before birth. The practice of branding is sometimes attacked
by humane societies, whose members do not stop to reflect
that by the momentary suffering of the calf the range areas

* From *The Georgics,* Book III (Brodribb's translation), published 1929
by D. Appleton Century Co., New York. Reprinted by permission of Ernest
Benn, Ltd., London.

are spared the cruel divisions of humankind that result from disputed ownership. You may be sure that if any other permanent method of marking bovine property had been discovered since Virgil it would now be in use. Branding, very simply, is necessary.

This takes place up our way about the middle of June, when the calves are big enough to stand it, but not too big to wrestle down. Their average age then will be about two months; some will be older, of course, and some younger. Calves of less than two weeks are let go until the fall, when they are taken care of with the slicks that come off summer range with their dams.

The old adage that "many hands make light work" is never truer than at branding time. A day is fixed, with an anxious eye to the weather (you must never put a hot iron to a wet coat, since it scalds), and you phone around, or if your country does not possess this amenity, you drive up the road and leave notes in the mailboxes. The missus has shared in setting the day, for it will be up to her to serve three hearty meals.

You rise before dawn, and in June that is very early, and you take all the riders that you can muster on the ranch. At daybreak you are at the outer limits of your pasture, and from there you ride in, gathering the cows and calves, which at that time are getting a daylight snack. If the distances are too great to gather on the day appointed, you will have gone out the day before; by all means take time for your drive and don't let the calves get their tongues out. Of the different classes of cattle, cows and calves are about the most difficult to drive; the cows fret about their offspring, which tend to trail, until when, with the best of intentions, you try to hurry them along, and then they will as like as not hightail it away from the herd. It is almost impossible to turn a calf on the run; it is best to let them go. Most of them will come back, but not infrequently one will light out like a startled deer, and crashing through fences and brush, keep on running until a mere speck in the distance. You will be best advised to let such a one go; you will not lose it, for the calf will by a sure instinct make its way back to where it last sucked its dam. You will have a chance at it again in the fall, but by then it will be plenty big to handle.

Branding on all but the biggest ranches is now done in a corral instead of on the range. For a small outfit there may be only the one corral, near the buildings; for a medium-sized one there may be two or more outside. To brand on the range requires more riders than are generally available, for not only do the calves have to be roped out, but the cow herd has to be held from drifting. Corral branding is easier on the calves, in that they do not have to be dragged as far by a rope; with a calf chute or a branding table, they do not have to be "busted"—by which is meant thrown down on their sides.

By the time that you get in to the buildings with your drag you will find a row of ponies hitched to the corral poles, and a line of sombreros on the woodpile outside the kitchen door. Inside there will be the clatter of dishes and the friendly palaver of your neighbors. You sit down and take on a bait. When you go out there will be a spiral of smoke from the corrals, where someone has started the branding fire, and you reach down your irons from the spike on the old cotton-wood.

But first you must have selected and had approved a brand. This, like the selection of a coat of arms by some knight of old, is a matter not to be taken lightly. If you stay on in the country, you and your brand will become known in ever-widening circles; in fact, if your cattle are good and the country likes you, your brand may even take you over, so that you become one with 7 D Bragg, or Bar U George Lane, or Lazy H Harwick.

The very best of all brands, the perfection to which all range men aspire, is a single character brand that is clear, distinctive, and that cannot be put on the wrong way. This last-named attribute derives its value from the circumstance that in the heat and rush of branding the iron is not infrequently put on upside down; anyone who has had occasion to manipulate an office rubber stamp knows how easily this can happen. A cow so misbranded may be an ambulatory advertisement of the iron wielder's ineptitude for as long as twelve years.

Examples of this ideal, irreversible brand are: The Pigpen ⊞, recorded in Texas; the Bug ⚉, of Montana; the Double H ⊢⊣ and the S wrench ⟡, both of which belonged to Henry Miller, the great cattle king of early-day California.

The beginner with a talent for design can amuse himself by trying to find something in this category. If he succeeds he will then have to get it accepted.

Time was when your fancy in brands would be accepted without question by your state recorder; now freedom of choice has, as in many other ways, been restricted. The recorder is not infrequently an aloof person who has an office in the granite capitol and is apt to frown upon anything in the romantic line. You have to be very persuasive to wheedle out of him an arbitrary character brand; he will tell you that all such have long ago been taken up. He will balk even at two character brands, and try to get you to accept three characters, and those standard numerals or letters. But with persistence, and a close study of the Brand Book—the Domesday Book of the range—you may get something like your heart's desire, although you may have to accept, pending the attrition of the recorder, something taken prosaically from the alphabet.

Your neighbors will have memorized most of the brands within a hundred-mile radius, a feat which you on many occasions will come to envy. I tried it in my first few years at the trade, limiting myself to the brands used between my ranch and the railroad, but I gave it up when I found that it was easier to ask my ten-year-old son, who, when praised for the feat of memory, looked puzzled and said that he hadn't learned them, but just "knowed them up."

It is quite true, as J. Frank Dobie says in his *Heraldry of the Range,* that the youngsters know their brands before they know their letters. He tells of one youngster who heard at school the rhyme:

> Twinkle, twinkle little star!
> How I wonder what you are
> Up above the world so high
> Like a diamond in the sky.

And thereafter studied the stars by the hour to try to make out the A ◇ brand.

Each letter of the brand alphabet has its declension, which the range man reads almost by instinct. Thus a letter can be either lazy or crazy, flying or walking, swinging, rocking, or tumbling. It can be benched, forked, circled, or anchored. Take, for instance, the letter L. It is thus declined:

| | | | |
|---|---|---|---|
| ∟ | straight | ∟ | rocking |
| ⌐ | lazy | ∨ | tumbling |
| ⌐ | crazy | ∟ | benched |
| ∪ | flying | ∟ | forked |
| ⊢ | walking | Ⓛ | circle |
| ∩ | swinging | ∟ | anchored |

When you have got down pat your declensions of the letters, you can then learn the various styles of earmarking.
These are, in part: the crop, the under round, the over round,
the under slope, the over slope, the under split, the over
split, the swallow fork, the swallow tail, the steeple fork,
and the jingle bob.

In your choice of a brand you should avoid one that is
too easily altered, i.e., where one or two simple touches of
a running iron can change it completely. It should also avoid
angles that are too oblique, or lines that cross, for then it
will blotch. My first brand was, for instance (after my ini-
tials) ℬ. It blotched badly at the center, where the two
lines cross, but I had to continue with it until, by the inter-
cession of a friendly legislator, I secured my first choice,
which I have run for these many years. It is ℛ and is read
"rattlesnake crazy R." It is easy to apply, does not blotch,
and is easy to read.

With its issue to me I was able to carry on a brand of my
father's, although with a lapse of four decades. He located
in the early eighties a fine range on the Canon Ball River in
North Dakota, but it was then in the heart of the Sioux territory, and the increase of his herd went with discouraging
regularity to the tribal jerky racks. He changed his brand
(which is seldom done) by putting the rattlesnake over his
initial; this at first accomplished its purpose, but, the buffalo
still declining and no Sioux having got bitten by the rattlesnake, the old trouble arose, and Dad pulled stakes and
drifted into other business.

This association of your brand with some episode in your history may help to spread knowledge thereof and minister to your pride. An instance of this is the 6666 brand, well known in Texas. It was acquired by a cowboy named Burk Burnett in a poker game. He had had a long run of luck that evening, and was bucking a rancher who had a good string of cattle and a good location. There came the time when the latter had played his last chip. J. Frank Dobie relates the story thus:

"Burk," he said, "I'm broke, but I'll play my ranch and cattle against your pile."

"You've made a bet," was the reply.

On the deal Burk Burnett drew two sixes. He discarded three other cards, keeping the pair. Then he drew two more sixes. The four sixes won the ranch. Immediately, Burnett rebranded the cattle he had won with his lucky number— 6666. In time he increased his holdings until he had three hundred thousand acres in the Indian Territory stocked with four sixes cattle, besides an enormous ranch in North Texas. An oil field came in on his land and a boom city named Burk-burnett sprang up. When his widow died, she left several million dollars to Texas Christian University—probably the best poker hand that a Christian institution ever drew.

If you can't get from the recorder what you want, you can thumb through the Brand Book and check those which most nearly meet your idea. You can then correspond with the owners to learn whether any of these are for sale. You will probably be answered, if at all, by indignant noes until perchance you come upon some old-timer, stove-up and retired to town, who can be persuaded by your cash. There are many brands recorded where there are no cattle to match them with; the reluctance of cattlemen to sell a brand proceeds from both fear of fraud and pride of ownership.

At the same time that you acquire your brand it is well to provide for its venting (cancellation) according to the laws of the state or province. This is usually accomplished by placing one character of the brand in a lazy position immediately below.

In some regions cattlemen use earmarking or wattling as a secondary means of identifying their cattle. Where a number of brands are run together, as on a national park or on a national forest, such auxiliary marking is almost essential, if the range be a northern one. By the time of the fall roundup, the coats of the cattle have become so shaggy that it is hard to read a brand on them. Wattling or earmarking greatly aids identification.

✿

Branding is a term that covers four operations—branding, dehorning, inoculating, and castrating. Your crew will be organized accordingly, with at least one man assigned to each job. In addition there will be the men to bring the calves in, and to bust them. The quickest way, and therefore the best for the calves, is to cut the cows away from the calves,

and rope out, on foot or horseback, in the calf corral. About
the fewest you can get by with for this is three men—two to
rope and one to wrestle down. The last-named is the most
strenuous of all; if it were not for the challenge to the pride
of the lads in their prime you would have hard work filling
the job.

The bottleneck in branding—to borrow a current industrial term that fortunately hasn't yet reached the range—is
in the roping. This is an art in itself and goes well if the roper
is in good form, but all artists have their off days. If I could
instruct you in roping by the printed word, I would have long
ago set up a correspondence school. About all I can do is to
tell you to get a hard-lay rope, make a loop in it (avoid a
metal honda) and practice.

The branding fire should be made of dry wood, cut to
length, and there should be enough of it so that the job does
not have to be halted for firewood. It is best to put it in a
shallow trench, and lay the handles of the branding irons
over a log, which will keep them cool. The hypodermic
syringe for vaccinating against blackleg should be in a mild
disinfecting solution, and plenty of vaccine to carry through
at hand. The knife should be sharp, and with its own bowl
of disinfectant. The man to dehorn will have his dehorning
spoon (or knife) and the caustic stick. The tally board, with
its pencil hanging by a string, should be at hand. When the
irons are hot, when everything is snugged up shipshape and
Bristol fashion, then the boss of the outfit, looking over his

crew, can raise his voice above the bawling of the cattle and shout, "Let's go!" Then the production line swings into action; the roper dabs a loop about a calf's head, drags it forward; the wrestler grabs it with one arm around the neck and the other hand on the stifle, and with an expert heave and thrust of the abdomen throws it on its side; his helper runs up and, sitting, grabs one hind leg and thrusts against the other with his boot, the dehorner runs up and cuts the small horn buttons and applies the caustic stick, the branding hand runs up with the hot iron (and they should always be nearly red hot, being thus much more humane) and stamps the brand, the inoculator runs up with the syringe and gives the shot that has come to be necessary on almost all western ranges, and the man with the knife starts the castrating. If your helpers are experienced, the job runs smoothly, and at the rate of fifty to sixty calves an hour. It is plenty hard work; the sun of summer beats down, and the dust rises and swirls, and the sweat runs down in rivulets. Here if at no other time a man's temper is apt to run short, and the boss in particular must watch his tongue. Welcome indeed is the dinner gong, when the fire is banked, and all hands strip to the waist and splash in the cooling water, and go in with an appetite such as only that kind of work can give.

When the job is over it is best to move the cows and calves immediately to pasture before the calves stiffen up and get logy from the vaccinating. They should not be moved too far, however, and if their summer pasture is too remote, they should be dropped off on near-by grass, where there is plenty of water. They can be picked up the next morning and taken on.

It is a vast satisfaction to have your own branding out of the way and your tally in your notebook—so many steers and so many heifers. You know then what you have produced for all your labor and expense during the preceding twelve months. You go on to your neighbor's branding with a serene mind.

✿

The physical work of branding is not perhaps as severe as in haying or in pitching bundles, but it is considerable, and it is perhaps well to dwell a moment on this aspect. The man who is following a sedentary form of life may well recoil from the prospect of sore muscles and a stiff back such as he occasionally experiences when he has to do something strenuous. It may well be that never in his life has he performed physical labor long enough to have experienced the glow of health, the sense of well-being, that is the reward of that kind of living. This sense is transcendental to such a one, using that word in its philosophical meaning, and as such cannot be described; that man will probably prefer to do his ranching vicariously, which, in the abundance of western stories and western movies, he can do, particularly if he hasn't too critical a judgment. But, in order to allay the fears of the man who has at some time worked hard out of doors and then gone soft, I would point to the amazing adaptability of the human body. If you are, let us say, under fifty, have nothing wrong with you organically, and have not allowed your muscles to stay entirely flaccid for decades, I believe that you can adapt yourself to the demands of a ranching life, providing always that you are sustained in your exertions by a liking for the kind of country in which ranching is done. That of course applies the whole way through. If everybody who has contemplated a ranching life had entered it, or even if everyone who has entered it had stayed with it, you would not now have your chance at it; range land would then be worth more than Iowa corn land, and cattle would be the cheap by-product of a kind of strength-through-joy movement.

Hours of hard physical work do of course preclude hours of mental activity, and the sense of tedium is not always absent. Your muscles will get sore at times, no matter how fit you are. The weather will not always be to your liking; in fact, the worse it is the more necessary it is for you to be outdoors, for it is then that your livestock most need looking after. Range country is for the greater part high up, and therefore, being without benefit of the masking haze and mist of lower altitudes, a country of extremes. Nothing is more certain than that at certain times of the year you will be either too hot or too cold. As I write this it is too cold, and I look out on a snowy landscape lying bleakly under a watery sun. My two men are out feeding cattle with a sleigh; this afternoon it will be up to me to relieve one of them so that he can work with the colts. It is below zero, and in such weather I have not yet discovered a way to keep my hands warm on the handle of a pitchfork. But I know that the remaining cattle will get fed, and that I shall come in to a warm supper in a friendly room, and that I shall have a sound sleep— unless, that is, our best saddle mare, whose romance flowered at the wrong time last year, chooses this night to foal.

But it is about time to revert to the life of the critter, whose career as your piece of property legally begins when he gets branded.

Any disability that the calf may suffer as the result of his treatment in the corral is of short duration—with, of course (if he was a bull calf), the one exception. His friskiness is generally restored within twenty-four hours. From branding to weaning time in the late fall he exacts the minimum amount of care of his entire career. His dam at first gives him all his food; after about two months on a straight milk diet he begins to nibble at the grass, and by November the roles of milk and grass are interchanged; it is then that milk becomes the supplement.

The care of your herds in summertime consists chiefly in surveillance from horseback. These rides through your herds on their quiet summer ranges with a warm sun overhead and green grass underfoot are the pleasantest part of the business. They can, by being interspersed with the heavier summer jobs such as fencing and hoeing up the potatoes, give relief therefrom.

What you look for in your riding are such things as these: Is there any infection of the calf's brand? (This is very rare up our way.) Is the cow giving enough milk for her calf? How is the salt holding out? This should be before cattle at all times. Are the cows chewing on old bones? If so, a phosphorus-bearing supplement such as bone meal is indicated. Is the water supply in good shape? A good water supply, summer and winter, is as important to cattle as good grass. Have your bulls ganged up? If so, then you must break up their gentlemen's club and push some of them to the outer limits of your pasture. Have stray bulls broken in or have your bulls got out? Have yearling heifers, which, as I have said, should not be bred, broken into your breeding pastures? The propensity of heifers to seek out a bull is one of the greatest sources of ranch trouble. To obviate this, many ranchers send their heifer herd far away in summertime, up in the mountains, with a cattleman's association. Have stray bulls broken into the dry pasture, that is, into the pasture you have reserved for yearling heifers and for cows which, in anticipation of their sale as beef next year, you do not wish to have bred? A dry cow fleshes up on grass; not so a nursing cow.

What is the state of your fences? If you find one broken down you stop and toggle it up with the aid of the fencing tool that you carry in your saddlebags at all times. How about poisonous weeds, the distribution and toxicity of which vary from month to month? Do the feet of some of the cattle need trimming? (The same question applies when riding through your horse bunch.) What sign is there of predatory animals? For us this question has, of recent years, with the increase of game in the national park but six miles to the west, come to be a serious matter. Has any critter got porcupine quills in its nose? This is liable to occur in those pastures having brush patches.

You will, in the course of the summer, find animals that, because of quills, or bones stuck in their throats, or feet gone bad, or for some other reason, will need close attention. This can be given either by throwing on the range or by bringing them into your corrals and there putting them through your chute or squeeze. To rope and throw alone an adult animal on the range, without injury to critter, horse, or rider, demands experience and skill. It is a job that the newcomer should tackle only with a companion and two good cow ponies. When riding alone, and trouble is discovered, it is best to drive in the animal.

This summer riding, this inspection of your grazing herds, demands alertness, and for the first few years of your career you may be so intent upon catching all details that you do not find time to look about you. But, with practice, wider powers of observation can be acquired, by virtue of which you will miss no detail but will still have time to enjoy those pleasant aspects of the country to which your city-bred companion, riding beside you, will devote his entire attention. You will even see more of the wild flowers, the bird life, the game, than he.

Your summer pastures will, in number and size, depend upon how many and what kind of stock you are running. The simplest form of ranching is carried on by what is known as the steer man, who buys young steers and grazes them out to sell at heavier weights. He will need but one large pasture. If you are on a cow-and-calf basis, that is, if you sell calves in the fall after weaning, you will need just two pastures, one for your breeding herd and one for your dry cows and replacement heifers. If you sell steers, you will need a third pasture for them, for it is poor business to run steers and breeding cows together; the cows are constantly being bothered by the steers, and the latter do not flesh up properly. If possible you should have a separate horse pasture and, of course, the near-by barn pasture wherein to keep your milk cows and the saddle and draft horses caught up for work. Some considerations on proportioning and fencing your pastures will be given later.

The calf should be weaned when it has nursed its dam from six to seven months. Her milk supply will then be drying up; she will need a little time to put on flesh before winter sets in, and her calf within her is demanding more of her vitality.

Weaning is very simply accomplished by driving into the corrals the cows and calves and cutting out the calves. At such time the children's music lessons are suspended; the women put cotton in their ears, and the men get hoarse. You don't have to break up at an early hour your evening reading, or games, or plaiting hackamores, or repairing saddle gear; you won't get much sleep. The bawling of the cows outside the corrals is matched by the bawling of the calves within.

Fortunately the process does not take more than a few days; it is speeded up if your corrals are so arranged that the cows cannot get up and smell their calves through the bars. During weaning you should have before the calves at all times your brightest and best hay, for the transition from a part liquid to an all-dry feed diet is not without its effect, and the calves lose weight which they do not recover for at least a month. The calves should have good clean water before them at all times, also salt. It is best to keep them in the corral until they have forgotten all about their dams, then to put them out on winter grass—i.e., grass that has cured and has not been grazed—and within a well-fenced pasture. This may be the same pasture that was used for calving out in the spring. In this connection, by keeping a tight fence around your calves, you will not have to contend later with breechy or fence-crawling cows and steers.

It is the almost universal practice now among small or medium-sized ranchers to give their weaned calves some kind of supplemental feed, such as hay or grain, or commercial protein concentrates. There is considerable labor and expense involved in this, but it pays well in ready-to-market weights. The practice of the old range outfits was to let the cows wean their calves; this is not desirable, for by the time the cow kicks off her calf, she has usually been dragged down too far in weight. Then some range outfits weaned by gathering cows and calves and then cutting out the calves, which were hazed off in one direction at a run, just as far as they could travel, while the cows were run off in the opposite direction, preferably behind a range of hills. A man was then put out to riding line between them. He, however, could not always keep the two from getting together again. The calves wintered out on the range, on grass alone, and there was a not inconsiderable loss.

Until the next spring, when they become yearlings, the calves will be designated by the term "weaners." This may lead the newcomer into some confusion, as when old Mr. Klug told my wife that he had been riding for a week looking for six weaners, and she magnanimously offered to give him, if he would come to the house, six pounds of her home-made sausage.

Opinion differs greatly among ranchers over how much feed to throw into weaners; the yardstick is the total gain made during the winter. Some maintain that it does not pay to feed more than enough to keep them at their weaning weights in the fall; that the effect of fifty or one hundred pounds of gain, expensively made, is lost in the course of the next year or two. The Manyberries Range Experiment Station in Southeastern Alberta has tried dividing a bunch of calves "down the middle," feeding the one group so as to make substantial gains in weight, while the other is fed only enough to keep their weaning weights. The two groups in the spring were turned out on the range together, and each was weighed up that fall, and again the following fall. There was no difference in weight at either weighing.

I have never performed the same experiment, but I have followed through our various groups of calves to the ages of two and three years. Those fed meagerly (following dry years when we had light grain crops) have never done so well as those fed so as to make appreciable gains, and the latter definitely made heavier marketing weights. In our case, with home-grown grains, the economy of winter-feeding calves some kind of supplement to hay and grass is indisputable. What form your feeding will take depends on the district and on the prices of the various kinds of supplements available, such as oil cake, cottonseed meal, brewers grain, etc.

The nutritive value of livestock feeds in relation to their prices is too lengthy a subject to admit of proper treatment here. There are many good feeding manuals available. There is one safe principle, in following which you cannot go far astray, and that is to raise as much as possible of what you need. This will turn you at certain times of the year into a dirt farmer, or, in the terms of the old cowman, a sodbuster, and as such, in bib overalls, with a grease can in one hand

and a monkey wrench in the other, you will earn seasonally his contempt—and sometimes your own. But the ability to feed your cattle well when necessary (their first months as weaners is the most important of such times) will give you an edge in the business.

✤

When you have brought your weaners through their first winter you will have by then given them the greater part of the attention that they exact during their lifetimes. You will be able to turn steers and heifers out on their summer pastures with the certain knowledge that, if the rain descends from heaven, they will grow and prosper. Heifers and steers can be run together that first summer if necessary, but it is better to separate them even then. Your steer range should be the best grass available; steers weigh up more heavily than heifers of equal age, and sell for more per pound, having a higher dressing percentage.

At this point, if you have a quota in a community grazing organization, you will find yourself in a dilemma. You will then have your choice of whether to use this quota—be it on national forest upland meadows, or on the public domain, or (in Canada) on the national parks—either for your cow herd or for your steers. It is better to use these high pastures for your cows, for the kind of grass that grows there, lush and soft, is a better producer of milk than of beef. It is the hard grass of lowland pastures that puts a hard finish on your steers. Yet by reason of the rough topography of mountain pastures, you will not get as good a calf crop, for the bulls do not so readily find the cows, some of which are sure to seek out some hidden little spot—a gem of a place from their viewpoint—and there hole up for the entire summer, and so do not get bred. Then, alas, it is an ingrained trait of human nature to reserve the best effort for what makes for individual profit. So, into community breeding herds your fellow ranchers are inclined to turn in their poorest bulls.

If, however, you keep your cows at home and send up your steers, they will not make the gains that they would if kept nearer home on harder grass.

The way to resolve this dilemma is to see to it that your association herd is managed so as to constitute a good breeding area. This entails the appointment of an authority empowered to cull the bulls to be turned out, and to enforce the order, and the employment of a conscientious rider who will spend all waking hours in the saddle, seeing to it that none of the cows get pocketed, and that salt is put out frequently and in the right locations.

I have spoken before of the advantage conferred on a ranch by the accessibility of summer grazing to the public domain. It is perhaps well here to emphasize the point. Grass is almost always cheaper on such ranges, for they have value only in summertime, and the government has not yet got around to levying taxes on itself. There is no competition with

the cattlemen for the use of such areas, unless it be by the
wild-life enthusiasts, who want the game to multiply until
it mantles the hillsides. There will always be a conflict of
interest here; the sensible way to resolve it is for the authorities to set aside certain upland areas, limited in extent, in
which no commercial grazing is allowed. The game can spill
over from such areas onto the cattle ranges and onto land
open for hunting. If left to itself, game will increase to the
saturation point, after which, in the absence of a sufficient
number of predatory animals, there is only starvation for all.
The presence of game in a country adds to its interest and
charm, and I would be the last to wish it to be reduced to
the vanishing point. On my own land I am almost certain, in
the course of a day's ride, to see game of one kind or another.
The mule deer are most abundant, but we also have elk and
an occasional moose. The sight of a white rump patch gliding
through a grove, or of a sleek form arching gracefully over
a fence, is a never failing joy.

I have mentioned the matter of replacement heifers, and
here, before leaving the subject as such, I should enlarge on
their selection. In a well-managed herd, as in a well-managed
vineyard, there will be pruning of old wood and a grafting
in of new. Cows reach an age where they begin to decline;
they either do not catch in season or, if they have a calf, they
do not raise it well. The retirement age for range cows is
from ten to twelve, although certain unusually sturdy individuals may last up to fourteen, fifteen, and even sixteen.

These declining cows, if caught and dried up while their teeth are still good, are valuable for sale as beef. They should be cut out at weaning (since at that time their calves will give the clue) and noted or marked so as to be identifiable the following spring. They may be singled out for especial winter care, by means of heavier feeding. They are not bred that summer, but are kept over into another, when they are again put into the dry herd, at which time, relieved of maternal duties, they will flesh up and become salable as fat grassers. If they do not calve the summer following their culling from the breeding herd, they will, of course, be ready for market that fall.

Cows should also be culled from the breeding herd, even if not yet of retirement age, if they show signs of being unthrifty or of being nonbreeders for more than one season.

Thus one has each year a certain number of individuals going out of the herd, and obviously, to sustain the predetermined numbers in the breeding herd, must introduce at the other end an equal number of replacements. These are selected from the yearling heifer bunch or the two-year-old heifer bunch. If heifers are carried over to the latter age, it is better to select replacements then rather than at the earlier age, as conformation can then be better observed.

Again, as in the selection of your bulls, you have a chance to exercise your talents as a judge of cattle. The thriftiest, blockiest, best-built heifers should be taken. Each year, therefore, you will "top out" your heifer bunch, keeping the best and sending the rest to market. It is always a temptation to reverse the process, but if you do your herd will show a progressive decline in quality and profitability.

If you withstand this temptation to sacrifice immediate profit for ultimate gain, you will have the great satisfaction of seeing your herd increase in quality, even to the point where it will be said of it, when under discussion by order buyers or breeding stock buyers, that "if you've seen one you've seen all."

The quality of your herd is the yardstick by which you will be measured as a cattleman. You can live in a sod hut, you can drive the oldest and most dilapidated car, you can even ride a plug of a horse, but if your cattle are good, then you are rated as one of the solid stockmen of the district. You will be listened to with respect, and at your ultimate passing you will be mourned.

✿

When visitors from the city are with us, and the talk falls upon the improvement wrought within a herd by selection of individuals through successive generations, someone is almost sure to exclaim:

"Now, if only the human race could get the benefit of the same treatment that livestock people apply to their cattle! What a wonderful improvement could be made in a short time!"

The analogy is, however, false. In breeding animals we

have narrowed our objectives within limits attainable by selection. Thus, what the dairyman wants is high milk production; what the hog raiser and beef producer want is a higher rate of gain, put on in the right places. With the single-minded pursuit of single objectives, the relatively inflexible material—germ plasm—that we work with becomes manageable.

But who shall say what should be the objective of him who undertakes the Olympian task of changing, by parallel methods, the human race? Before you launch into any program of development, you should have your goal in sight. Would you, in the human race, aim at greater tractability, more docility? Or is it reason that you want, or greater endurance? Do you want a man who is just intelligent enough to carry out orders, and yet not so intelligent that he "unto himself direction arrogates"? And what admixture do you wish of the qualities of the heart?

These questions may give some idea of the complexity of the task that faces the geneticist who attempts to control the mechanism of human heredity. He is stopped almost on the threshold of his quest because, if he is an honest man, he cannot define his objective. He can do something on the negative side, such as the elimination of mental defectives, but even here he must proceed with caution, for genius and insanity are sometimes not far apart.

I have dropped, among other youthful conceits, that of wishing to inflict upon humanity my own kind—or any other kind—of animal husbandry, and I have become deeply grateful for the rare flowering of the spirit that one meets in all walks of life, in all kinds of surroundings, and amidst all but the most demeaning of vocations.

## V. The Ranch Homestead

Let the Wealthy and Great roll in splendor and state,
I envy them not, I declare it:
I eat my own lamb, my beef and my ham,
I shear my own fleece and I wear it.
I have gardens and bowers, I have fruit, I have flowers,
The lark is my morning alarmer:
So jolly boys now, here's God speed the Plough,
Long life and success to the farmer!

(An old English farm toast)

**M**any a ranch homestead seems out of keeping with the
fortunes of the owner. You may see, in traveling about
the West, several thousand acres of good-looking grass,
dotted with thrifty cattle, and in the midst thereof a dilapidated shack or a log cabin sagging on its rotted sills. You
will wonder why a ranch of such size cannot support a set of

78

buildings at least as good as those you will find on the average eighty-acre farm in the corn belt.

The reason stems in large part from the nomadic tradition of ranching in the old West. The owner of a herd would locate a range, squat on the water holes or the hay land, and stick as long as the Indians would let him or until the homesteader came along. He did not expect his tenure to last a lifetime; rather, he expected to have to pull stakes and move on at intervals, the length of which was governed by circumstances more or less out of his control. He did not, therefore, put much money into buildings.

With the retreat of the herds to the nonarable land, and the stabilization of the business that came when the public land system gave way to private ownership, the old tradition did not die out; it persisted strongly enough in the breast of the cattleman to cause him to limit his house and barn and corral to the bare minimum, to something from which he could walk away at any time, throwing the key into the water hole.

When we came into the country we were just new enough to the business to be untouched by this tradition, and so we paid no attention to it, nor indeed to another which is almost equally deep-rooted, i.e., that you send all your good beef to market and eat only the oldest cows.

To be sure, our ignorance of range traditions did not end there; it was almost limitless, but most of the others, as our experience lengthened, could stand the test of reason. Not so these two; we still save out for our meat supply a fat heifer, and when we came we put a substantial portion of the money we brought with us into a house. We have never had cause to regret this, for in good years and in lean years we have had a tight roof over our heads; a warm haven in winter, shining its light out on the frosty ground when the day is done, and in summer a cool retreat when the sky is a bowl of brass overhead. It is a story and a half and by urban standards not large. It lies snugly in the lee of a hill that interposes itself between us and the mountains. We would have preferred to place the house on top of the hill, but the old-timers counseled us to forgo the view in favor of shelter from the wind. Range country in winter is usually windy country, and beneficently so, for the winds, either by melting the snow (in the chinook belt) or by blowing it away, uncover the grass. More of the chinooks later; they blow warmly but violently on our range, and we have to locate our buildings out of their racking path. The view of the mountains is always there; we have it before us in the day's work, and a two minutes' walk around our hill will bring it to us in the evening. We have come to feel that it is just as well not to see the mountains from our windows, since there is such a thing as living too intimately with grandeur.

What we see instead are the grassy hills, flecked with parklike groves of willow and poplar, rolling down gently toward the distant bald wheatlands. The hills change in color with the seasons, and they change in outline when the cloud shadows drift across them. In the morning and evening light, when the horizon is a deep color, these shadows take bites out of the crests of the hills, so that the sky line is completely altered. The same effect is produced in winter by a wind-storm following a snowfall; the depressions in the hills and the coulees are then filled with blown snow, and the ridges and crests laid bare. Where the milky horizon of winter meets these crests there is no line of demarcation. In murky weather or by night we are wont to navigate by such landmarks on the horizon as notches or humps, and when these are obscured we can easily lose our bearings. Jogging back from our railroad loading point on a snowy day I have gone as much as ten miles astray.

The view commanded by our windows is measured not in miles but in a score of miles, and although we have screened off the cordillera to the west, we still feel, in certain moods, as on an autumn day, a sense of oppression. This feeling is not unknown to those born to the life; it hits newcomers not infrequently. There is one sovereign remedy and that is to have below your windows, in the immediate foreground, something minutely perfect, something cosily intimate. It can be a planting of mugho pines, a bit of lawn, a flower bed. It may be nothing more than a bird bath, or a martin house.

The best of such devices, the one that will most surely relieve the austerity of the country, is a picket fence. There is something about the New England decorum of a picket fence that exorcises the feeling of oppression, of loneliness, of which I speak. My counsel therefore is that you put one around an area on the front side of your house. You can later plant within it what you will, as observation enables you to make a selection of what does well in the country. There are few ranch locations where something cannot be got to grow in the line of perennial flowers or shrubs. If you have water you can even have a postage stamp of a lawn. I know of nothing nicer upon coming in from a long ride than to take off your boots and stretch full length on the lawn, and to let the scent of the green grass and the white Dutch clover replace that of the sagebrush or mesquite, or the acridity of the trail.

✿

It is well, when starting from scratch, to locate your building as nearly as may be in the center of your land, so that your travel time, to and from work, may be reduced to the minimum. This obvious counsel will, I realize, not prevail in cases where there is some one spot on the ranch that captivates the imagination. Nor should it prevail; the enjoyment of such an ideal building spot will in the long run outweigh extra minutes on the trail.

I would not be so presumptuous as to tell you what your house should look like or how it should be arranged inside, except to say that all ranch structures should be kept as low of roof line as possible, not only for the practical advantage of being down out of the wind, but to be in keeping with range country, where the forces of erosion have ruled out anything with rectangular lines. A blocky, four-square house, sticking out on some hilltop, offends the eye.

Whatever your idea of an outside finish, nature will not be long in making it over into a neutral tone, for sun and winds are strong. I believe that it is best to start with an oil finish on wood, and thereby preserve the natural color. A shingle roof is to be avoided if possible, for shingles, although not rotting out as in moister climates, warp badly, and, as the saying is in the West, "spit out their nails." The new flexible composition roofings seem well fitted for the job, unless you locate in the Southwest and follow the Spanish style; there is nothing more appropriate to such countries, where the absence of snow makes it possible, than a flat roof.

The millwork exposed to the weather, such as window frames, sash, and doors, should be of the best clear lumber, even if this enforces economy in the interior trim. It is well to weather-strip, not so much against the cold of winter as against the dust of summer.

A word as to the so-called modern conveniences: In their contemplation you must remember that there is not one of them that does not exact its meed of mechanical attention, and when they break down, as they all do sooner or later, you probably will not find a repairman ready to hand. In fact, at the customary rate of ten cents a car mile, plus the going union scale, you may well find that you must buy your pump or lighting plant over again every two or three years, unless you possess, or can acquire, some knowledge of their mechanism. This is why a lot of ranchers who can afford them elect to dispense with modern conveniences, and why in some houses where they are installed you will on occasion find the bathtub used for storing seed grain, or gasoline lamps hung from electric light fixtures.

The knowledge needed to perform nine-tenths of the repairs need not be of a high mechanical order. If you can grind the valves of a gasoline engine, clean and adjust the spark plugs and breaker points, clean the carburetor and gas lines, install new generator brushes, clean and adjust relay contacts, cut a pump gasket, do simple pipe fitting, repack a gland, install new leathers, and a few other such things, you can get by fairly well especially if you keep a few spare parts on hand. A course in general mechanics at a trade school is a valuable precursor to a ranching or farming career.

The younger men in the country generally possess these skills; the older generally do not, so that you may find some well-heeled old-timer, who can read the brand of a critter by eating a steak from it, quite content to pack water and stoke a potbellied stove.

I would rate the modern conveniences in the following order of importance:

1. Running water.
2. Central heating.
3. Refrigeration.
4. Electric light.

This order applies to the northern zone; in the southern, items 2 and 3 should perhaps be transposed. I put electric light last in order, because there now exist very satisfactory gasoline lamps and lanterns, and, besides, artificial light will not be one of your major concerns after you begin to keep usual ranching hours.

All items on the list are nice things to have if you can afford them and can keep them in repair. None of them are indispensable to success or happiness in ranching. Many a fine outfit, where the cattle are blocky, the horses both lifey and manageable, the fences taut, and the hay meadows lush, is entirely without them. There is a point, as to modern improvements, beyond which you cannot venture unless the ranch is to become top-heavy with machinery, and you condemned to going around with the feeling that there is always some machine to be maintained, adjusted, or repaired. The same principle applies to taking on too many farming side lines or too many tractors or implements. Top-heaviness of plant over cattle is given by ranch economists as the most frequent source of ranching failures.

It is not quite as easy on a ranch as in the city to become the prisoner of your possessions, but it can happen. It is prone to happen to those who attempt to duplicate all the conditions of their urban existence, and it usually happens to ranches on which oil is struck, an event which not infrequently means misfortune for the land, and sometimes for the family thereon.

I did not place first on my list the radio because on all ranches this has come to be taken as much for granted as the automobile; together these two have in large part banished from ranching and, for that matter from farming, the sense of isolation. The one brings many of the amenities of civilization to you; the other takes you to them. In the case of the radio you will have to acquire, before you can really profit by it, the faculty of falling into a mental vacuum while the commercial plugs are being given, for in ranching you do not so much make money as avoid spending it (with comparable satisfaction in living) and the radio is frequently a circean voice beguiling you from your course. One evening, when we were finding it difficult to resist the blandishments of an announcer who had some particularly enticing gadget to offer, a neighbor, who had had supper with us, told us of an occasion when, being in town, the grocer had urged him to try some papaya juice, saying that it was most delicious. He answered:

"Mister, I got so many tastes now I can't satisfy that I don't aim to take on any more."

Since then, when something has become too beguiling, we dub it papaya juice.

With judicious dial twisting, one can get programs that range from the satisfying to the thrilling as, for instance, when without changing from my overalls and denim shirt I can enjoy a symphony concert for which, in a city, I would have to don a boiled shirt. There are excellent news programs timed for the noon and evening hours. There are market reports that help one judge when to start off with the beef drive for the railroad.

As to the automobile, I should like to caution you that the presence of this tool on a ranch can easily betray the owner into squandering many hours—and dollars—in unnecessary travel. There is a spurious sense of mastery, especially after you have been riding a horse or driving a team, in taking the wheel and coursing over the countryside. This sense properly belongs to those who built the car—the metallurgists, the research, designing, and tool engineers, and the production managers. For the rancher, such a sense is legitimate only when he has succeeded in turning out a finished cow horse or a good draft team.

An advantage of modern conveniences is that, having them, it is easier to entice to the ranch interesting visitors from the city. We find the people who come to us congenial and interesting, supplying experiences and observations complementary to our own. I would say that, in contrast to the popular belief, ranch and farm people welcome and like city people —those, that is, who make an attempt to understand the rural ways of life. We know that, in order to have consumed the vast volume of produce that we put on the market, there must be heavy concentrations of population in the cities, and we know that this entails great economic and social problems, which must be solved if the fabric of society is to hold together. The solution is up to the city people. The group that creates these problems does not, unfortunately, seem to be the one which attempts to solve them; it is from the latter that we draw our visitors, and it is to us a great source of satisfaction to observe the refreshment of body and spirit that we are able to give them. We have had such visitors as the chairman of a Red Cross unit, the doctor of a general children's clinic, the minister of a large church, together with their spouses and children. We always keep on hand two gentle plugs for them to ride, of that complete gentleness that goes with an utter lack of ambition. On these animals (currently an aged gelding named Jerry and a mare named Dinah) our visitors amble over the hills and drink in a view and soak up the sunlight. In time we promote certain of our visitors to helping out with the less exacting jobs, such as holding a cut of cattle. We even permit some to spray for potato bugs, and to irrigate in the garden, which gives them a chance to get bare feet in the squshy mud. In the evening they tell us of their work, and of what is new in books and art and music. We know that it is but natural that some of our children will find their lifework in the city and, conversely, that some of the visiting children will, in the normal healthy interchange of rural and urban population, want to go on the land.

As to fashioning the interior of the ranch house, that again is a matter of personal taste. One should always keep in mind, however, that the dwelling is only in part your personal shelter and retreat. For the other part it is ranch operating plant. You cannot draw a sharp line between the two. I might add, in case the matter ever comes up, that the income tax inspector also finds it difficult to make this distinction.

Your house will not only minister to your personal needs as to shelter, warmth, and food, but also for the needs of the sick and injured of the ranch hands—and in the course of time there may be not a few of the latter, for the business is not without its risks. It must even be impressed at times into ministering to the needs of the ranch livestock—notably at lambing time (if you keep a farm flock of sheep) and at chick-hatching time. Certain parts of the ranch work go on within it, such as the repair of saddle gear, the mixing of veterinary formulas, and, in the spring, the germination tests of seed grain. At that time, if your diplomacy be equal to the task, your earth-filled tomato tins displace on window sills the cherished house plants.

For these reasons, the house should not be cut up into too small divisions of space. The kitchen should be rather more spacious than in a city house of the same size. It should be so located that its windows give upon some scene of ranch activity, as the yard or the machine shop or the corrals. The tedium of the kitchen routine will thus be relieved and an awareness of, and sense of participation in, the work of the ranch will be engendered.

Whether you will have a fireplace in the living room will probably depend on how abundant firewood is in the vicinity. A grate fire is a source of good cheer, but not of much heat, and if fuel be scarce you will probably want to save it to stoke up a good rotund potbellied stove, preferably one with isinglass windows.

✿

The ranch barn will vary with the country and the climate. Here also it is best not to build with too high a ridge line. This can best be done by using a central hay well, so that your hay storage starts at the ground level instead of above the plate, at the level whereof your roof can begin, either straight-pitched, Gothic or gambrel—of the latter two types the gambrel can be more easily braced against the winds. The trend in farm barns is away from the larger structures, one factor being the development of hay-chopping machinery, whereby much hay can be got into a small space. Another factor is the realization that horses are better off outside, even in cold weather, and should be stabled only for the periods necessary for hitching and unhitching, and for feeding.

There are many different plans for barns available from such sources as the U.S. Department of Agriculture or from lumberyards in farming communities, or from barn-equipment suppliers. It is difficult to make a selection without a background of experience, and a barn, unlike the corrals, is not absolutely necessary at the outset. One can get along with a homesteader's shack skidded into position near the house, or one can nail together something that has a double stall for a team, and a single for the saddle horse, and a pen for the milk cow.

When the barn is built, I should advise against scrimping on materials, and on the dimensions of the interior units, such as grain bins, passageways, and stalls. Better to have fewer of these and have them adequate in size, and strong enough to withstand the inevitable accidents that come along, such as when a colt kicks at a stallmate and hits the partition, or when a harnessed horse catches his tugs in some projection.

The barn should have a section floored with concrete, and with stanchions, for the dairy. The keeping of milk cows on a cattle ranch is still, in some ranching districts, an innovation. The milk supply on some outfits still comes from a can, and the old rim-fire, grissel-heel stockman views a milk cow with as much repugnance as a pair of bib overalls. The contemporary rancher does not as a rule share this view.

There is nothing like a small string of milk cows ambling in from pasture at night to give a ranch the look of stability, and the folks thereon a feeling of permanence. The milk that comes from a live cow instead of a can is a lot tastier. The West has been described as "the place where there are more rivers and less water, more cows and less milk, and where you can see farther and see less." You can't do anything about the water situation, but as to the scenery you can cultivate the habit of observation, whereupon the emptiness is filled with interest, and as to the milk, you can tend a few dairy cows.

The disappearance of the old-time, one-purpose cowboy has helped out the milk situation; most ranch hands now expect to do chores, which includes the morning and evening milking.

In designing the ranch barn it is well to have stalls and aisles of ample width. The aisles I like to have nine and one-half feet wide, so as to permit a team to be driven in abreast and be unhitched out of the wind and cold. A single stall should be about ten feet long from aisle to outside of the manger, and about five feet wide. This width enables one to walk in alongside a saddle horse carrying one's saddle.

To keep the ridge line of the barn low, I favor the central hay well, with the horse and dairy stalls, the loose boxes, granaries, and saddle room ranged about the outside. Such a central well need not be kept filled in summer and fall, thereby giving extra room for such activities as fanning seed grain, repairing harness, and sharpening mower knives.

When in winter this central well is half filled with hay, the children can jump from the roof of the stalls into its fragrant and resilient depths. Some such jumping place is the inherent right of all farm or ranch children, and as for me I confess that it serves in winter the same purpose as our little lawn in summer; on coming in with the team or saddle horse, I not infrequently stretch out on the fragrant surface of the hay, and in the falling darkness listen to the wind over the ridge and to the soft barn noises within.

Your set of corrals are the single most important part of

your ranch plant. Here again, as in the choice of a barn plan, the permutations and combinations can be almost infinite in number. The least number of pens that one can get by with is three. The biggest is your receiving corral, into which you put your drive upon coming off the range. This should be so located that the cattle are not spooked up by unusual noises and sights as they are being driven in, and should preferably have two wings veeing out from the entrance gate toward the direction of the drive. This corral should open into a small crowding corral, from which the cattle chute, with its squeeze at the far end, debouches. Then there should be a holding corral, to receive and hold the animals that have gone through the chute. There should be a by-pass around the chute, so that calves, for instance, can be cut through it away from their dams.

It is well, but not essential, to have two subsidiary corrals opening off the main holding corral. Into these can be put various cuts from the herd, as steers into the one and heifers into the other. The holding corral (or corrals) should preferably be supplied with water; a single trough can be made to supply two or even three of these by being placed on the dividing fence or in the corner.

A roping corral, octagonal or round in shape, is a desirable adjunct, particularly if one is running a bunch of horses. One can stand at the snubbing post in the center and rope out his mount. This roping corral can be placed within the main receiving corral or at one side. The main, or receiving, corral should be big enough to contain the entire cow herd, unless this herd is so large, or so scattered, that working corrals out in the pasture are justified.

The matter of drainage should be considered when locating a set of corrals; if the soil is not absorbent (a gravel flat is best of all), the location should be on a gentle slope.

The corral should be stoutly built, and at least six feet high. The materials of construction will vary with the country you locate in. The best kind of rail is the lodgepole pine cut up in the mountains where a fire has killed a stand; when pine poles are not available, one will have to go to the expense of buying two-inch plank in town—preferably undressed plank. By all means use the pine poles if you can; not only are they cheaper and more satisfactory, but their procurement affords a legitimate excuse for taking the family up camping in some green mountain meadow.

The panels of our corrals we prefer to make sixteen feet long; the corral posts should be set solidly in the ground— three feet of depth is not too much. The use of pressure-treated posts is recommended for those who can afford the initial cost, as they last forever. One can greatly lengthen the life of home-cut corral and fence posts by treating them at the ranch. Untreated, they rot out from fungi at the ground level. We chop down green poplar or quaking aspen trees, cut them into sections of proper length, peel the butt ends, and soak them in a concrete vat filled with a saturated solution of copper sulphate (bluestone). At the time the butts are peeled we also peel a strip up one side; the greenish solution follows the sap upwards, and when the color shows up in the peeled strip, which is above ground level, the post can be taken out of the vat, and is then ready for use. Thus treated, posts last for a long time—just how long I cannot say from firsthand observation; the first use of this process, which gives us posts that are immeasurably cheaper than any kind that we can buy in town, was eight years ago, and those so treated at that time show as yet no evidence of decay, in spite of the fact that our climate is a good deal more moist than that of the average ranching district.

I have always been at a loss to understand why so many ranchers are content to go on year after year replacing rotted-out corral and fence posts with new posts that will rot out equally fast. The job is a chore which most ranchers accept resignedly, as they do the vaccination of calves—something they cannot get out of. An engineering friend, who has traveled about a great deal in ranching country, was equally at a loss over this phenomenon; he calculated that if all the corral and fence posts replaced each year on the ranches of North America could be assembled in one pile and burned the Btu.'s evolved would exceed the combined output of Vesuvius and Mauna Loa.

✿

The residence, the barn, and the corrals are the most expensive items of the ranch plant. There will, however, be other subsidiary structures (not all of which need be built at the outset) such as the combined shop and garage, where are kept the materials and tools for ranch repairs, and a chicken house, and, of course, the bunkhouse.

When starting in new, it is well to build the bunkhouse of the same materials as your own house, and provide it with the same facilities; that is, if your house has electric light, the bunkhouse should have it, and if you have running water, the bunkhouse should have a basin and a shower bath. There will be many occasions when both you and the men will come in dusty and sweaty, and they should have the same chance to clean up as yourself. The bunkhouse on a ranch is all too often some discarded homesteader's shack, towed up and toggled up to make shift with, or an old log cabin that has stood since Indian days.

A good ranch hand is worthy of good housing and fair treatment. In the quality and attitude of the hired help you will have, if you manage properly, your advantage over the large outfits. The hired man who works at the owner's side, who sits at the owner's table, who has the children of the ranch tagging at his heels while he does the chores, who is tended by the boss or his wife when sick or injured—he it is who will take a direct and personal interest in the welfare of the ranch. This close association provides the bond of interest that gives you as the employer not just a certain number of hired hands, but hired eyes, and ears, and brains.

Let me give an illustration of what I mean: I have sent a

man out riding to check up on the bulls in a certain breeding pasture—that is, to break up any gathering of bulls, to put out strays, to reclaim any of ours that have got outside. An old-time, one-purpose cowboy would do this job and do it efficiently. But my man will do the same things with equal efficiency, and he will take care of details that the man who considers himself a rider and not a ranch hand would either not deign to notice or, if noticed, would consider no part of his duty. My man may have seen that a salt trough had been kicked open; he will fish out a few nails from his jeans and nail it up with his fencing tool and then scoop back with his hands the spilled salt. Or he may have ridden through our horse pasture and have noticed that the wires on a certain section of fence have come loose. Whether he will then stop to draw them taut and restaple will be a matter of judgment. The fence will hold the located horses, i.e., those that were born on the place or have been there long enough to have come to consider it their home, but it will not hold any horse that wants to get back to the place where it was foaled, to its *querencia*. If there be such an animal in the pasture, my man will stop long enough to fix the fence, even though I am awaiting him at home. Better to keep me waiting an hour than to condemn me to a ride of twenty miles out and twenty miles back to repossess a stray.

The type of cowpuncher who works as a rider for a large outfit would probably deem it below his dignity as a top hand to nail up the salt trough, and he probably would not stoop to the fencing job, although to retrieve the strayed horses he would cheerfully spend the next two days in the saddle. If the joint operation with his employer which was awaiting him back at the ranch was something like, let us say, spreading manure on a hay meadow, you can be sure that he would string out until dark any riding job that he was put to. Back home the next day he might think of the broken salt trough and the loose fence and report them to the foreman, in which case the foreman would have to send out a wagon with a ranch hand, and by the time he got around to doing this the salt would have been washed away or trodden into the ground, and the new colt in the pasture have pulled out. The big outfit would have allotted to these two simple jobs two men and a wagon to accomplish what my man has taken in his stride, and to the time of the two men there would have to be added the time of the foreman while giving his attention to this job.

In such ways, and in other similar ways, the bigger ranch is handicapped. It may have other offsetting advantages, such as better grass (which is most likely since the big ranches are usually those located in the earliest days) or better water or a location nearer to market. But good management is necessary to take advantage of the best of natural conditions, and this cannot be given (any more than in urban industry) without good workers. This handicap of which I speak, that of putting on two men where one could do the job, would be cheerfully accepted, providing the outfit could get the men at all. As to those not still in the armed forces, the competition of short hours and high pay in the city has drained away most of the men who know enough of ranching ways to be of value; the money wage that the rancher can afford to pay will never come up to that set under the dominance of urban labor. As to hiring those who remain, we of the smaller spreads are better off than those of the larger. The man who remains is most likely of the general ranch hand type, who is so much a craftsman of his particular trade that he dismisses any thought of a change. The place where such men want to work is in general the family-sized ranch, where a white woman and not a Chinaman does the cooking.

The present stringency in ranch labor is only the accentuation of a trend strongly in evidence before the war; the fact is that many other less exacting ways of earning a living have come along since the old days, including several million new government jobs. And then the more adventurous type of boy, who makes the best ranch hand and who had hitherto been available to step into the boots of the stove-up older man, has had other vistas of choice, such as in aviation, opened up to him. At any rate, even before the war, the cowpunchers were simply not there for hiring in the necessary numbers, except in the strip along the Mexican border, where lives the *vaquero*, who, knowing no other means of livelihood, does not walk the fence as a horse transported to a new range.

In thus calling attention to the superiority (for our purposes) of the domesticated, all-purpose type of ranch hand, who will do anything within reason that you put him to, I wish it understood that I am not disparaging the one-track type of cowboy—he who will punch cattle and break horses and do nothing else—either as he now exists on a few isolated ranges or as he lived in the free and glorious eighties and nineties and the early 1900's. I knew him once—oddly enough in northern Mexico where a large American landowner kept a small army of them to ensure his survival during the revolution. I have read a good deal about him. My feelings toward him are mixed. I am glad that it has not fallen to my lot to manage him, that is, to try to get from him the kind of work that must be done on a place like mine, but I have a strong measure of respect for him.

I have come across and marked in my reading a description of the early-day cowboy that is so apposite that I am tempted to quote it in full. It is taken from a book by John C. Van Dyke,* an art critic and a trained observer, who, from a strong love for the grandeur and austerity of the plains, roamed Montana in the eighties.

In the order of their importance, and in the estimate of the cattlemen, the cattle came first, the horses next, and the men last of all. If anything was to be rescued it was the imperilled herd, not the men. The cow-punchers could look after themselves, hustle their own horses, rustle their own beds and food, and get out of trouble as they got into it. In Montana,

* *The Open Spaces,* copyright, 1922, by Charles Scribner's Sons.

in the eighties, they were all young, active, and capable, needing neither sympathy nor help. And, naturally, astride of a horse, wearing "chaps" and carrying a gun at the hip, they took themselves rather seriously. They even accepted the popular estimate of themselves that they were a distinct genus of their own, and a bold bad lot into the bargain.

I never had many delusions about the cowboy, for I knew his kind before he was born. He never belonged to the Mexican *vaquero* class in the sense of being raised with cattle and riding with horses all his life. The *vaquero* was a peon herdsman, born and trained on an *hacienda,* and remained such to the end of his days; but the northern cowboy was merely a Wandering Willie, who rode the ranges for a time because it was an easy job. He was usually a ne'er-do-well. Born perhaps in the Mississippi Valley region, and rejected by his family for moral delinquencies, he drifted out on the border and became a ranch hand because help was scarce and anybody could ride a horse, drive a cow, and tote a gun. He rode for only a few years and then, getting stiff in the joints from many strains, he took up with some kind of trade, opened a livery-stable or a saloon, started prospecting, gambling, tramping, or some other honoroble or dishonorable calling. Cowboying was to him only a youthful and a temporary stop-gap. The raftsman of the Mississippi had typified his kind a dozen years before him. They were both of the unsettled youthful class and took up with riding a raft or riding a horse because the work had excitement in it and not too much continuous exertion.

The mentality and morality of both classes were rather conspicuously absent. They had little or no education, no great intelligence, and the very slightest sense of responsibility. The vices of the border town—drinking, gambling, women—were naturally uppermost with the cowboy. Occasionally I would meet one who could speak the truth without swearing, and almost all of them recognized property rights and abstained from stealing; but they were quick on the trigger, shot to kill, with no compunctions of conscience if they happened to succeed, and got out of the country on a stolen horse if it were necessary.

They partly atoned for these reckless propensities by an unbounded good nature and generosity. The morose and disagreeable personality was seldom met with. They all talked a great deal, as young people usually do, and their theme was naturally limited, especially on the range. In a cow-camp every one talked cow or held his tongue. The tenderfoot from the East who started in to discourse about the theatres or restaurants or society life in Chicago or New York soon found himself without an audience. They knew nothing about things east of the Mississippi, and they did not care to know anything about them. They talked their shop and wanted you to do the same.

Of course they were generous—that (rather than patriotism, as Doctor Johnson had it) being the last refuge of a scoundrel. Almost all crooked people are generous, and everybody, straight or crooked, in a new country where people are scarce, helps his neighbor. Those who live in crowded cities, and struggle to keep their ribs free from their neighbor's elbows, have very little understanding of the right and decent feeling among people who live in the open. Helpfulness with them is not so much regarded as a virtue as selfishness a crime. The cowboy, as a class, was never selfish. I had one summer for a partner a boy who had killed two men, been a gambler, served a term for stealing, and had a decidedly bad record; but I never knew a more sunny nature or a more generous one. When we rolled out our blankets on the ground at night, if there was one side softer or better than the other I got it; when he reached for the coffee-pot he helped me first; when we saddled up he would rope and bring out my horse or swing my saddle. And with all his bad history he was tremendously courageous and had as much endurance as any man I ever knew.

This same cowboy, while riding with me on a round-up and trying to cut a cow and calf out of a herd, had the misfortune to be badly thrown. The calf ran across and in front of his horse while going at full speed, and the result was that both horse and rider turned a complete somersault. The cantle of the saddle caught his right leg, making a square break of the ankle. That was bad business, for we were eighty-four miles from Miles City—the nearest place for medical help—and no way to get there except on horseback. I was the only one in the outfit who had ever seen a broken leg. I got the cowboy—we will call him Dave—down to the creek, stretched him out, pulled off his boot, found the break, and by much pulling and more awkward feeling got the broken sections into place. I had brought from the grub-wagon a cracker-box, which I split up into many thin splints, and also several flannel shirts that I tore into strip bandages. I made a plumber's joint over the ankle, winding it until it was nearly a foot in diameter and reached from the instep to the knee. The whole was lashed fast and tight with much heavy cord and rawhide. During this crude performance Dave never flinched or groaned, though the sweat was rolling down his face; but when it was finished he swore with much violence and thanked me between oaths.

The real difficulty now came. It was the height of the season and even I was riding down and out three and four horses a day. Dave had to ride alone to Miles City because no one could be spared from the round-up to go with him. I put some cold provender in a small gunny-sack, caught up an extra lead horse, got him into the saddle, and started him across the Big Powder to Miles City. He got there, as I afterward learned, without accident, but it must have been a difficult journey. It meant that he had to get in and out of the saddle, picket and water his horses, gather his wood, make his fire, cook his food, stretch his blankets, and all with a broken leg. He was four days and nights on the way, meeting not a soul, and sleeping with one eye open for fear he might lose his horses and be left afoot and crippled. That, I submit, called for courage and endurance. Few people would fancy the trip alone even unhandicapped by accident. Dave pulled through by sheer grit. When he got to town and had his leg examined, he was told that it needed no resetting. That was sheer good luck. He was back on the ranch in less than six months, quite as good as new.

The writer of this passage seems to have started off in a mood of disparagement, but, warming to his subject, to have ended on a note of praise. Thus it is that I react to the old-time cowboy. He was maddeningly irresponsible in everything except that which pertained directly to cattle and horses; his profanity was of that uninterrupted and diffuse kind that betokens a mind devoid of perception (he would, for instance, ride a range for ten years and not have the remotest idea of what birds there were thereon, or indeed if there were any birds at all) but taking him all in all, you can honestly say that he was some hombre.

I can parallel from experience the instance of Dave's striking out across country with a broken ankle. I was staying at a ranch in northern Chihuahua; an American cowpuncher came up to where the foreman and I were talking, and said that he had decided to drift. This the cowboy was wont to do at any time, for no discernible reason. The foreman pointed out to him that one hundred and fifty miles of plain and desert lay between the ranch and the Rio Grande, and the revolution was at full flood. The country was bedeviled by marauding bands of Villistas, of Maderistas, and their kind. The cowboy's answer was that he reckoned he could take care of himself, and the next morning we watched him pulling out across the vega, riding one horse and packing another, as unconcerned as a New Yorker taking a ride in Central Park. I have often wondered whether he made it.

The old-time cowboy asked no favors, and what commends him to me especially at this time is that he was not everlastingly on the prod, as most of the people in the cities seem to be, about his own security. I can survey the urban scene with some detachment, and the intensity of the search for security of various kinds—of job, of health, or of person —is both puzzling and alarming. Security is a mirage, and the intensity with which it is being pursued is engendering disunity and stagnation. The paradox of the search is that the more ardently individuals and groups and classes strive for security the less collective security there is to go around. Business asks for props and adventitious aids from government, and the farmer seeks security by forming Congressional blocs, and labor unions seek it in the closed shop and the checkoff. It is not hard from this distance to discern that in the frenzied zeal of these groups the rights and dignity of those who seem to get in the way are being trampled underfoot, and resentments aroused and injuries inflicted, and the basis on which the only true kind of security can rest, namely, a large volume of production in goods and services, is being undermined.

The old-time cowpuncher was not spooked up about his own security, and neither was his boss, and so in this land we had abundant and savory beef, with steaks and roasts at from twelve to fifteen cents a pound, with the liver thrown in. The present-day rancher is not generally as hell-bent-for-leather as was his predecessor, but he certainly does not put security uppermost; his trade involves a considerable amount of risk, both business and personal, and he accepts it, without (as to the personal) the assuagement of an accident insurance policy, which he often cannot get because of the degree of hazard. He is not the beneficiary of a pension plan; social security is not for him. He accepts also the fact that what he will have for his declining years depends on his present exertions; and, perhaps, upon filial loyalty.

I have called security a mirage and lest I be thought a cynic I hasten to direct your attention to the fact that the word "mirage" is not synonymous with "illusion," as the rider of a desert range comes to know. A mirage usually reflects something real, but in a false direction. Security can be both a mirage and a real objective, in that it is illusory but attainable. But we can't head directly toward it, for if we do we shall run into black lava and dry washes; the direction in which it lies is that of sustained and harmonious production of those goods or services which each of us best knows how to fashion. If we don't learn this lesson we shall have to learn its alternate, which is that we cannot legislate ourselves into ease and affluence.

If it is to be the latter, it will be the urban classes that will sit longest at the feet of that stern teacher, adversity.

I state this, I hope, without the complacency that might arise from the possession of herds and fields and the lore of the trade. Country folk in general, although they may take pride in their self-sufficiency, do not view with detachment the perplexities and sufferings of the city people. I have heard many a time some farmer or rancher's wife exclaim: "How terrible to walk the streets and not know for certain that you will have food, or that you can chop your own wood!"

We have got somewhat off the trail, which forked at the point where we were discussing the ranch bunkhouse, and I was counseling that it be endowed with whatever amenities the ranch house might happen to possess. Such divagations, I may add, are sanctioned by ranching precedent, whereby it is understood that you can take time off to palaver on some interesting topic, no commitment being inexorable except haying in summer and feeding in winter.

We had covered the greater part of the ranch homestead. I should, however, before closing the chapter, like to dwell for a moment on an attribute that makes the ranch more livable. This is the garden, which may be, and usually is, combined as to vegetables and flowers.

Here, on the family-type ranch, the break with tradition is complete, for the scorn of the old-time rancher for anyone who broke the sod was absolute. He seldom, if ever, planted anything, preferring to freight from the railroad all his grub, except for the home-grown beef, and this, for easy keeping on the roundup was, as often as not, salted or jerked. By now this tradition has been thrown overboard, and a ranch garden, with its adjunct, the root cellar, has come to be the rule, and summer and winter there appear on the table the vegetables which the old-timer scorned, and for his scorn suffered, if modern dietetic theory be correct, many ills. I myself cannot discern in the record any proof that the dietitians are correct. The old fellows sure could perform on their kind of diet. For instance, the man who located this ranch drifted up with his herd, in the eighties, across a hundred miles or more of foothills and prairie from Choteau, subsisting then, and for a half century thereafter, on a diet of beef, flour, salt, and saleratus. The log cabin, in which he led a bachelor's solitary life, we have taken care to leave intact on the river flat by the big cottonwoods and within, hanging on its peg, the frying pan which by rigid scruple he never washed out. I was accustomed to mention this to make the point, which I have always believed in, that dishwashing had no demonstrable value until, about the time the women-folks returned from a trip, the frying pan disappeared, not to show up again until an unusually dry summer exposed the bed of the river.

The ranch garden is no different from the city-lot garden, in that the degree of your enthusiasm for it reaches a peak with the arrival of the seed catalogues along about St. Patrick's Day; the profile of its curve thenceforth declines a little with the first weeding, more steeply with the second and third, hitting the bottom with the heat of summer, and then jogging upwards as the produce begins to roll in, until, with digging-up time for potatoes, carrots, and the other winter vegetables, it climbs back to the ordinate of its origin.

There is, however, this difference between the city-lot gardener and yourself; he can, after all, let go, the corner grocery being there to take care of his needs. You have no such choice, once you have accepted, or had forced on you, the convention that vegetables are necessary to health.

Hoeing in the garden is a mild sort of activity, and as such an antidote for the more strenuous ranch jobs, such as breaking out the colts or cutting cattle. It is, moreover, one which many of our visitors take to, especially when confronted in the morning with a lively saddle horse. For our garden we have irrigation from a flowing well, and this, conjoined with plenty of barnyard manure, ensures good yields, and the spreading of this water down the neat parallel rows is a task that all but the most bookish people enjoy.

When it comes to flowers—the cultivation of these up our way is a labor of supererogation. The wild flowers of the foothills grow abundantly in the normal season, and in great variety. A botanist has counted during an afternoon's ride as many as fifty-nine varieties in our pastures.

The procession begins with the hairy crocus, blooming in March or early April, first on the south slopes and then on the other exposures. A late snow may blanket them, but they emerge, with the thaw, still smiling. Their flowers are lavender, and from an inch and a half to two inches across. At about the time the crocuses are appearing on the hillsides the yellow avalanche lily begins to show in the swales, where it follows the edges of the retreating snowdrifts. Then come the cerise shooting stars and the delft-blue camas on the hay meadows, and on the hillsides in purple and gold the delphinium and wild sunflowers. In the willow thickets the climbing blue clematis comes on, and in the grassy openings the blue lupine and pink wild geranium, and the showy tiger lilies.

By this time the procession has become a stampede, with gaillardias, fireweed, monarda, paintbrush, and a host of others joining in. And, if this abundance is not enough, we can change our flora by riding up into the mountains, a matter of four or five hours at a cow-pony jog. The looking-over of our herd on their summer range gives us a good excuse for doing this; the cattle are never so well salted down as when the bear grass, or the sego lilies, or the penstemon bloom, or when the yellow and purple mimulus marches along on either side of the mountain brooks.

In this profusion there is little incentive to cultivate flowers around the house; nevertheless, the instinct that lies deep in all of us to force nature to perform at our bidding takes hold, and we plant such flowers as foxglove, Canterbury bells, and peonies, which are about at the northern limit of their range; these we grow with success. Their less hardy companions, such as the rose and gladiolus, we struggle with year after year, and when we are able to persuade them to bloom our rejoicing is great. In such manner I have seen the natives of the tropics, where orchids and gardenias and poinsettias are to be had for the stretching out of the hand, tending assiduously wan sprigs of aquilegia and lupine.

The wild flowers of our range are not the demure and reticent visitors of less favored climes; in their season they boldly take over whole areas. The showiest varieties are the tiger lilies, which can tinge a hillside orange; the gaillardias, which will turn a whole pasture slope golden; and the lupine, the most abundant of all, which can mantle the entire range in blue.

The reign of the flowers lasts during that range heyday known as greening-up time, from the spring thaw to about the first of August. Then it is that the cattle and horses look sleekest, and put on their fastest gains; then the Blackfoot Indians quit whatever jobs the inclemency of winter has forced them to take and get ready for their sun dance.

At length the rains taper off, and the range turns first to an olive hue and then to sage, and then, under the pelting rays of an unobscured sun, to the brown color which it is to wear, except when mantled or flecked with white, until the next spring. In its wonted austerity it forgets all about its flower-spangled ebullience, and as you ride you point out to the incredulous visitor where the masses of color lay a few short weeks ago.

But even then, if you seek such favored spots as the occasional soaphole, or the lee of a patch of buckbrush, you will find a few late-blooming flowers, like the wild hollyhock or the purple asters, which do not give up until the skies turn cold and leaden, and the winter of their discontent begins.

## VI. Fencing and Haying

The range man of the early days reserved the deepest vials of his wrath for barbed wire; for once he made common cause with the Indians, and solicited the aid of such nomadic retainers as the wolfers and the freighters. He fought barbed wire unremittingly, but, in the end, to no avail, for it had the unconquerable attribute of perfect adaptation to a purpose, which was, by the partitioning off of the range, to convert community property into personalty —a process that satisfies some deep-seated urge in the human breast.

It is a temptation to tarry over the history of barbed wire, beginning with the story (common to many epochal discoveries) of an undiscourageable inventor, the difficulties of an introduction to the market, the protests of the shocked humanitarians, and ending with the injunctions of all authorities, legal and quasi legal, *de jure* and *de facto,* and the destruction of the first fences by the aroused citizenry. But all this was, as I have said, to no avail, for by means of barbed wire the land-hungry homesteader could plant his crop with some assurance that it would be he himself who would harvest it, and not the cattle of the range man, and the small rancher could know that he could start up without the certainty that his livestock would drift away with the larger herds of the range or that the hay meadows which he had taken pains to develop would not be overrun when the new hay was ankle-high. And it was barbed wire in the hands of the purebred man that made possible the establishment and survival in the range areas of the seed stock that was to transform the commercial herds. The early-day range cow was in sad contrast to her present-day descendant. She was a cat-ham'd, swaybacked, brockle-faced, and ewe-neck'd critter, and so high off the ground that she could straddle a hitching rail. She went on reproducing her kind with the assistance of bulls selected at roundup time by the process of letting go uncastrated every fifteenth or twentieth bull calf. But when barbed wire came along, the man who had the ambition to improve his herd could segregate it and keep it from outcrosses.

Barbed wire is not nice to handle; it has a malignity that

knows how to bide its time, so that there is not, I venture to say, a single rancher who has spent five years at the trade who does not bear its scars on hands, wrists, or forearms. I have already spoken of the injuries that it inflicts upon horses. It should be handled with stout leather gloves, preferably gauntlet style, or with leather wristlets. It comes new in eighty-rod rolls, which have a hole in the center, through which as a spindle a crowbar can be thrust. It can then be mounted as a hurdle on a wagon box, and the wire will unroll as the team is driven along. By mounting four such spools, the strands of a four-wire fence can be laid simultaneously; but one man should walk after the wagon to see that the strands do not tangle on the ground.

You may have occasion to handle reclaimed wire, as when moving a fence; a half-mile length can be towed over grass by a team, or around a corner, if a steel peg be used as a turning point. It can be coiled up in secondary rolls, by a knack that can be learned on the ground. Never, never, lose your temper over barbed wire; never jerk at it; always plan its handling with deliberation.

I have got somewhat ahead of my story, in that before one comes to handle barbed wire the fence posts must be in place, and before that the line to be fenced must have been surveyed or picketed out. Picketing in open country is simple; it is somewhat more difficult in undulating, and almost impossible in terrain badly cut up by dry washes, coulees, or ravines. In such a case you had better hire a surveyor, lest your fence come out crooked, and be a reproach to you ever afterward.

To picket you should have in sight a point of origin and a point of destination—wherein rural practice in picketing sometimes differs from urban. These two points may be the corners set by the original government survey. A peeled stake head-high is set up on the one point, and another such on the other; by sighting between these two, as over the sights of a rifle, one can line in an assistant, who plants the intermediate pickets.

Fence posts can be either set or driven. The latter method is the more rapid, but the more arduous, since, to drive a line of posts one has to mount the tailboard of a wagon and swing a fourteen- or sixteen-pound sledge. The driving of posts can be done only when the ground is fairly moist, and it is well to start each post with the point of a crowbar. Driven posts are in general not so firm as set posts, so that in building a fence by this method it is well to set a heavier post every four rods. I have already expressed myself on the subject of treated versus untreated fence posts, and here again enjoin the desirability of using the treated.

For a proper and permanent fence, four strands of wire are used, and posts set at one-rod intervals. This makes the fence shipshape, although on temporary fence lines, or on seasonal leases, one is justified in fencing somewhat more lightly. The remaining details, such as the construction of gates, the bracing of corner- or gateposts, the weighting down of strands in the swales, and the degree of tension to be applied, one can best learn from observation.

There will always be the question of how many gates to put in. The law of your state or province may specify a minimum number, and their location, as on road allowances. If you put in just the minimum number, you may inconvenience the wayfarer, particularly if your fence happens to cross some old trail. This may be so dim that it may have escaped notice, but you can be sure that it will have been etched into the memories of the old-timers, and of the breeds, and of the Indians. If you fence in such a trail you may come out some morning to find your fence cut. Also on the side of putting in more than the minimum, there is the consideration that when your cattle get out, as they will sooner or later, you can put them back more readily if you do not have to push them too far to some corner gate.

Against putting in more than the minimum number there is the inescapable fact that the more gates you have the more often will they be left down by some careless traveler. Of all causes of vexation and delay on a ranch, this is prime. Cattle and horses will quickly spot an open gate, and file through it, and you as their owner are thenceforth condemned to a weary search.

The offense is all but unpardonable. Consider what it may lead to: You have gathered up in the mountains an early cut of beef. In so doing you may have lathered up two or three good horses in sashaying down the mountain slopes, and have risked your own neck to boot. You have taken the cut twenty, thirty, or even fifty miles to the ranch, and have there thrown them into a home pasture, awaiting the drive to the railroad. The season on grouse opens the next day; you have forgotten about it until you ride out to gather and find that the gate has been left open, and that your steers have high-tailed it back to the mountains. Or you have carefully cut out your yearling heifers, and have put them into the dry pasture. Then some picnicker from town, hurrying back before dark, leaves a gate down and the heifers, among whom there is no such thing as maidenly modesty, make for the breeding pastures, and you have the whole weary job to do over again.

Such utter waste of time in a busy life provokes the rancher's ire as nothing else can do, and turns him in the summer season from a genial out-of-doors man into a crabbed misanthrope. I know how the stockman felt who inserted this advertisement in the *Coastline Dispatch* of San Juan Capistrano:

> Notice: Positively no more baptizing in my pasture. Twice here in the last two months my gate has been left open by Christian people, and before I chase my heifers all over the country again, all sinners can go to Hell.

All in all, after much cogitation, I would recommend that one proportion the number of his gates to the distance of the ranch from town, or the frequency of fishermen or hunters or picnickers. If you are far out, and there is no fishing or hunting near by, you can be liberal with the number of gates you put in; otherwise you should be chary of them.

You must bear in mind that, however well you build your fence line in the first instance, it will always exact a meed of maintenance. No fence ever stands long by itself without some kind of attention. Sound construction minimizes this but does not eliminate it. Wires will snap in the winter's cold, or else will contract and then sag with the return of the sun. Staples will come loose as the fence posts dry out; fighting bulls will break off posts; a flash of lightning will touch off a stampede. A substantial part of your time, even under the best conditions, will have to be devoted to keeping up your fences. If you are fortunate in the character of your neighbors, the upkeep of the line fences will be shared, but your internal fences—cross fences, in ranching terms—are strictly your own concern.

The most unexpected things can happen to fence lines. We have, for instance, a line that runs along the bank of our river. We put this line in new, in three days of strenuous effort, using fresh unpeeled poplar posts. After the job was finished I went away and did not see the fence for a week or more. When I again rode that pasture a full quarter of a mile of the fence lay prone, each post neatly cut off about one foot from the ground. A glance showed it to be the work of beavers. A family of these industrious animals, probably migrating downriver from the mountains, had come upon what must have seemed veritable manna from heaven. From the relative age of the cuttings, the beaver had worked from the upper end of the fence downstream. One can imagine their dismay when, after cutting off the first post, they found it impossible to drag it into the river, and so to their winter's food cache. But, undaunted, they had returned to the task, and the second post had been neatly felled, and hanging on the wire, had proved equally unmovable. They had then felled the third post, and the fourth, and so on all down the line.

As an experiment, I drove in new green poplar posts for a few rods, and a few days later found that these had also been cut down and left hanging.

Since that time I have had more respect for the beaver's industry than for his intelligence; I have tended to compare the exhibit on this occasion with certain ambitious projects of humankind, directed to ends perhaps as enticing, but condemned to equal frustration. What the beavers should have had was some wise old banker beaver to counsel with. I can imagine his speaking to them, hands folded comfortably over an ample paunch:

"Now look here, boys; there's no percentage in this for you. It's the other fellow's game. You try something that hasn't got so many strings on it."

I could have used some such advice myself, on one or two occasions before I learned the economic facts of life, among which is that the banker, although perhaps never attaining the heights of business inspiration, has yet acquired the faculty of predicting what is likely to come off and what is not. His is a trade that I would not particularly like to follow, but I would recommend to the beginning stockman an occasional call upon the banker of his railroad town.

✿

The experience with the beaver befell us, as I have said, along our river, which bounds the ranch to the east. It is a pleasant clear water stream, and any of our ranch jobs that are situated on its banks are certain not to be slighted. The river has its source in a large mountain lake that fingers in between the peaks, and receives the rivulets that drain the ice and snow fields above. Some ten miles from the lake the river enters our land, crystal clear, cascading merrily over ledges, foaming over boulders, coursing around miniature islands, eddying into backwaters where lie the cutthroat trout. It is a highway for beaver, mink, and otter, and a flyway for such aquatic fowl as the harlequin and merganser ducks, and the ousel that walks under the water. For us, the second family living along its course from the austere peaks, it is a place of refreshment. We have many a picnic on its banks shaded by cottonwood and willow, and we fish in it, and, for a few fleeting weeks in the height of summer, we swim in it. But its greatest charm does not lie in such calculated pleasures, but rather in quick glances as we ride on its banks into its blue waters, or pause to stretch out for five minutes on its green margin, or else sit gazing idly at its flood, fixing the eye, perhaps, on the precise spot where the water curls smoothly, lightly striated, over some hidden boulder. From a long-buried classical education there once sprang to mind the lines of Keats:

> The moving waters at their priest-like task,
> Of pure ablution round earth's human shores.

The river is steeper in gradient where it enters our land than where it leaves it, some four miles below. It cascades no longer, but spreads out over shingle bars, where in myriad facets it reflects the sun. Its voice is subdued but still audible, and its waters are no less clear. Farther below, out on the prairie, it picks up, little by little, the load of silt that is to discolor its waters all the way to the sea, until by the time it reaches the first city on its banks, one hundred miles below us, it has a brownish cast. There it is subjected to its first indignity at the hands of man, being compelled to receive the vile burden of the sewers. We cross it by bridge when driving to the city, and we see that it has lost all ebullience of spirit, rolling sullenly along, without spume or crest, as if resigned to its adult labors.

Not far below the ranch it leaves the parklike zone of the foothills and courses through the brown prairie. Its channel, though hidden between the cut banks, can be followed from an eminence by the thread of green cottonwoods, until these merge into the far horizon.

✿

Of fencing, it can be said that, although there is always a certain amount to be done each year, the times for doing it can be selected according to convenience. No such choice is permitted you in the case of that other ranch job, which, with fencing, constitutes a major ranch activity. Haying has to be started when the hay is ready, and, once started, must be carried through to completion. This job is, of course, the most important of all. You can miss a gathering of beef in the fall, and the steers will still be there for attention later on. You can even miss a branding, and the calves will still be following the dams at snowfall, and can, with somewhat more effort, be branded then, or they can be sold as slicks to someone who will put his own brand on them. But if you miss haying you will be unable to carry your stock through the winter as they should be carried, and sooner or later you will hit one of those disastrously severe winters which ruin the improvident or unlucky stockman.

The proper time to cut alfalfa is when it is about one-third in bloom, and timothy or brome when it has just finished blooming. Other varieties should be cut according to species. In timing the start of haying one seeks to secure what the agrostologist terms the maximum in total animal nutrients. If hay is cut on the green and tender side the protein content is higher than later, but bulk is sacrificed, and on balance there is a loss. The season in which one should cut is not long, in either event, and if one misses it, the loss is irretrievable, for when any kind of hay (except perhaps for native bunch grass) is sere and dry it has lost most of its protein and minerals, and, unlike native grasses, is practically worthless.

To hay rapidly and successfully requires a good deal of preparation and organization. The extra teams should be got in from their pastures, and have their feet trimmed, and possibly shod, and their harness adjusted. They should be driven around (particularly if they are to be turned over to children) until they have lost their snortiness. For this gentling-down process do not hitch them to haying implements, for these are dangerous under such conditions. The rake, to which the ranch children are most often assigned, is particularly dangerous in that when the driver is thrown from the seat by a runaway he usually falls in front of the teeth and is rolled over and over, and possibly spiked.

The various haying implements should be carefully gone over. This overhauling should have been done during the leisure of the previous winter, but it rarely is. The principal implements for haying are, in the order in which they are used: the mower; the dump or side delivery rake, the bull rake, sweep, or loader; and the stacker. All cracked or broken parts should be welded or replaced, all loose bolts tightened, and everything oiled or greased up. Mower cutter bars in particular need attention as to alignment of bar and sharpness of ledger plates and knife sections. The hubs of rake wheels should be examined for cracks, and for wear of bushings, and the mechanism for tripping adjusted, and new teeth inserted where necessary.

Hayracks should have the running gear examined, and hubs greased, and the baskets should be started out with all floor boards in place, and staves and rails intact. Hay loaders should have their endless rope assemblies checked for frayed or broken strands, and driving wheels and pickup teeth examined. The hay stacker, a breakdown in which will sooner or later bring to a halt all gathering and loading, is of especial importance in the scheme; it is well to renew the hoisting cable or rope at the slightest sign of wear, and the sheaves should be examined and greased, and the teeth or nets repaired.

At this point in the discussion of haying implements I shall tarry a moment to get off my chest a stricture against the poor quality of agricultural implements, which is responsible for the loss of much time by the rancher, and for that matter by the farmer too. One who, like myself, brings to ranching some previous experience with modern machinery is at first amazed and then angered by the obsolete design of farming implements, which seem to stem directly from the blacksmith rather than the automotive age. Bearings are often iron against wood, or iron against iron, with inadequate oiling facilities. Standard thread bolts are used where there should be machine bolts, and gray iron castings where alloy cast iron is indicated, and alloy cast iron is used where there should be forgings, and carbon steel forgings where there should be alloy steel forgings, and there is no health in the whole contraption. It is not that the implement companies do not know how to design modern machines, for most of them turn out tractors that are thoroughly modern and last a long time.

Breakdowns of agricultural implements are incessant, and usually occur at the time of maximum use, such as haying or grain harvesting. Hours lost at such seasons are precious and irreplaceable; the hay loses its succulence or the grain grows overripe, and the crew you may have hired sits around in idleness. Such breakdowns hit the isolated rancher harder than the farmer, who generally lives closer in to supply depots and machine shops.

When I have undertaken to reproach implement company officials for the quality of their product I have met the answer that farmers do not know how to repair or maintain more complicated machinery, or I have been told that the farmers always insist on a rock-bottom price and will let quality go by the board. I doubt whether they are right in either contention, and I think that an opportunity awaits the company that first brings out a line of implements of modern design.

The succession of jobs in haying is everywhere the same, but the variants of method are many and it would take a small treatise to encompass them all. In general, the methods may be classified in accordance with the degree of mechanization applied. As short a time as ten years ago the all-horse plenty-of-hands method predominated, and now there are few ranches that do not use at some stage or other power-driven machines. The change has been forced by the rapid advance in wages, and the shortage of men willing to do the heavy work. Now that it has been established, however, I doubt whether the trend toward mechanization will ever be reversed.

Many arguments can be adduced in favor of the use of horsepower (literally speaking). One of these is that horses are carried cheaply, and as a form of power are self-perpetuating. In using them the rancher is not continuously paying tribute at the filling station.

Against this is the fact that with power implements one can get up the hay rapidly, when it is in prime condition. This necessity of rushing the job to completion invests haying, in spite of the fact that it comes in the heyday of summer when the grass is greenest and the flowers are at their height, with a certain grimness. But in our northern zones the weather at this season is liable to be spotty, and a crew can be laid up days on end, and when the skies clear there is great satisfaction in being able to get up thirty to forty tons a day. Then, although the bills from the gasoline companies are liable to be large, they come only at the one time of the year, and the rancher is not always careful to offset against them the amount of grass that the idle horses eat all the year round. The average ranch has steady use for only one or two teams, and the surplus horses are turned out for all but the few weeks necessary to the haying operation. It is generally conceded that one horse will eat three times the amount of grass that a cow will, and this grass, at decent beef prices, can much more profitably be used for bovine rather than equine support. You may add to this the fact that horses are by far the most frequent source of accidents on a ranch, and an accident is not only a painful but an expensive thing. Such have to be accepted in the course of cowpunching, for working cattle cannot now, and I sincerely trust never will, be done except on horseback. And so in spite of the fact that a hay meadow full of well-matched draft teams eager and up on the bit is something to delight the heart of the stockman, and that the exhaust fumes of a tractor mask the sweet scent of the new-mown hay, I am afraid that I shall have to cast my vote, at least under present conditions, for the greatest possible degree of mechanization.

The reiteration of the superior economy of tractors helped to soften, but did not eliminate, the regret within our family circle that followed the decision to sell off the surplus teams. The sale of horses from a ranch is always invested with sadness. This even applies when the horses to be sold have never enjoyed much popularity; at such times even the most jugheaded nag becomes invested with some saving grace of manner or form.

It was then a solemn moment when the trucks backed up to our loading chute to take away the horses we had decided to sell. The women and children were standing around, and there was many a furtive dab with handkerchiefs. I had almost wished that we had not grown out of the strictly one-family type of ranching, wherein with but one extra hand we had put up the hundred and fifty tons that then sufficed for wintering our herd, and we did not have a tractor on the place. The beginner in ranching need not be in a hurry to leave this stage.

This tendency to make pets out of the livestock is something that the rancher with a family will always have to take into consideration when ordering his affairs. It invests ranching with a community of interest, but it creates problems. Thus, when in the fullness of time we came to slaughter a heifer of unusually mild and friendly disposition which we had fattened in the corrals for many months, we began as usual upon the more perishable items. The first to appear on the table was the tongue. One of the children pushed away her plate and burst into tears:

"Just think of all the times that little tongue has licked my face!"

But the arithmetic of mechanizing our haying was inexorable. In an all-horse operation we used to employ, in putting up our four hundred and fifty tons, fourteen teams—some hired for the occasion—and from twelve to fourteen men. The duration of the job (depending on the weather) was from fourteen to twenty-one days. With our present system we use two tractors, three teams, and eight men, and we generally finish up in ten days. In mowing alone, the tractor will get over thirty to forty acres a day, whereas a horse-drawn mower, even with a change of teams at noon, can do but ten.

The succession of the various jobs is, of course, the same whether machines are used or not. First comes the mowing. The hay is left in the swath until it has the proper degree of dryness. It will take a certain experience with your particular kind of hay and with the local climate to be able to judge this point. If hay is raked up too green it may mildew in the windrow or fire in the stack. If raked too dry, the leaves, wherein lie the greatest nutritive values, will shatter and fall off.

The rakes then follow the mowers at the proper interval of time. In raking the horse is making his last stand, the loads being light and therefore not demanding much power. The usual practice is to rake the swathed hay into windrows just a little on the green side, and there to let the hay cure further. In windrows it is not so easily moistened by a shower, but if a heavy rain catches it at this stage it must be turned over once or twice.

From the windrow the hay must be got to the stack, and this can be done in a number of ways. Pitching on to hayracks by hand was common ten years ago; then, when the husky young fellows who used to be available for this work began drifting off to the towns, we began to use the mechanical hay loader, which is towed behind the racks. This elevates the hay and it is then leveled off on the rack by hand. Either of these two methods has the advantage of permitting the hay, once it is on wheels, to be moved considerable distances, and thus large haystacks, in which the ratio of spoilage (by weather) to volume is the least, can be made. In many ways it is better to build larger stacks and fewer, i.e., stacks holding from forty to seventy tons. On every ranch there are certain natural locations for haystacks, either for the advantage of proximity to buildings or feeding grounds or of shelter from winds.

Large stacks do, of course, exact more labor, and so of late years have largely been given up in favor of smaller, located right on the meadows, to which the hay is bucked by horse-drawn or power-pushed bull rakes. This method is the swiftest and cheapest, a fact that is recognized by all authorities. Where the hay is at all sparse, as on natural meadows, the stacks so built will be from medium to small, because the capacity of the bull rake is only a fraction of that of the rack, and therefore more cycles between the windrow and the stack must be made.

The bull rake, I should explain, is a basket or cradle mounted on wheels and balanced on its axle. The basket has long wooden teeth rather widely spaced, and is pushed into the pile of hay to be gathered. The teeth with their burden are then lifted from the ground, either by the counterbalancing weight of the driver (in the case of the horse rake) or by a mechanical linkage (in the case of the power rake). The load is then rolled up to the stack, where it is dropped upon the teeth of the stacker or upon its hay nets.

There are many varieties of stackers, operating on different mechanical principles, such as that of the crane or the catapult. Each has its particular merits, and there is little profit in a detailed discussion, except that I might say that my preference is for the overshot stacker. The function of all is to get the hay up on top, where a man spreads it uniformly, and in such a manner as to give a slight overhang as the height increases. As the stack approaches completion it is "topped off" so that it will shed rain. The man on the stack has the single most responsible job in haying, and the most strenuous. If he "takes it straight," i.e., works without relief through the haying hours, which extend from the time the dew disappears to a seven-o'clock supper, he will have turned in a feat of stamina that a professional athlete will have cause to envy.

As to having athletes on a ranch—we have on occasion taken on for the summer a lad fresh from athletic triumphs at college. With the brashness of youth—to my mind a commendable quality—he becomes possessed of the ambition to show the boss, or the hired hands, what a good day's work really is. We take care, for the sake of our horseflesh, to assign him only short jobs on horseback, but for the rest give him his head. The day starts bravely, and the chips literally fly if he is on a fencing job or the hay cascades into the racks if it be haying season. The grizzled veteran working at his side is shown to be all but senescent; his measured motions mark him, even at a distance, from the youngster at his side. But before the sun really begins to pour it on, the athlete interrupts his exertions ever more frequently to take pulls at the water bag, and from ten o'clock on his energy comes in bursts, dwindling in frequency, until by early afternoon he is casting bemused looks at the shade patches under the racks or into the cool depths of thickets. When the boss happens by at such a time and offers the athlete a shift to a barnyard or garden chore, the stigma which in the morning would have made the thought intolerable will be found to have vanished into the thin western air.

If the athlete is still with us by late summer he will have learned to proportion his exertions to the all-day demands, and even under such conditions the veteran will usually be able to turn out more work.

As a matter of fact, although I should prefer to think otherwise, athletics, whether college or postcollege, do not always constitute the best preparation for a ranching career, as one might naturally suppose. This is probably because there is absent in ranching, except in its exciting phase of the rodeo, the stimulus of competition. No one is there to cheer you on or to inspire you to greater effort, and the rewards of the work are seldom in immediate sight. In fact, in haying this reward does not come until the succeeding winter, and one has to possess much imagination to visualize, as the perspiration pours off, a white landscape, locked in the embrace of winter, and a string of cattle on the meadow lowing their hunger to a cold and milky sky.

There are in addition to the standard haying methods outlined in the foregoing other new and promising systems, such as that of the pickup baler. This machine, towed by a tractor and having a self-contained power unit, picks up the hay in the windrow, bales it, and kicks it out onto a trailer towed behind. The trailer is detached at intervals, and is hauled to a central storage point, where the bales are skidded up to form cubical masses. The bull rakes and their drivers, the stacker and its skinner, and the man on the stack are thus eliminated, being replaced by two men on the baler and one or two on the trailer. The hay, being baled, is salable as such if more than proves to be necessary has been put up. If the central haypile has been properly topped off or roofed over, there is no spoilage with the passage of time. The hay can be fed out much more easily in winter. Thus, our neighbor to the south, Walt Jenkins, who uses the pickup baler method of haying, never has to keep a team caught up in winter, but does all his feeding with a saddle horse.

There are also on the horizon (as yet somewhat distantly for the rancher) other even newer methods, such as the forced drying system, wherein hay is hauled directly after cutting to a drying and compressing plant. This results in a high carotene content, which, however, is not so important for the beef producer as for the dairyman.

Whatever method you choose, at whatever pace your horse-power, manpower, and equipment permit you to proceed, do not neglect to put up each year *all the hay you can.* The new-comer, observing some neighbor's field dotted with many stacks, turning browner year by year, shrinking steadily in size, may be misled into thinking that he can rest from his labors when he has accumulated a stack or two above what he figures to be necessary for the succeeding winter. He can here miscalculate badly. Sooner or later there will come one of those prolonged and bitter winters that serve the range people as a time marker for all their lives and their children's lives, and then you will be profoundly thankful for a reserve of hay. At such times hay on the meadows is very much better than money in the bank, for then hay skyrockets in price, and even if it can be obtained it can seldom be hauled to where it can be used. Many a new rancher just getting on his feet has been wiped out at such a time by the lack of a reserve supply—yes, and many an old-timer too. Each range section has its story of a cattleman who, in the bitter winter of 1887, or 1901, or 1919, watched his string shrink to skin and bones, and then go down one by one, no longer to be tailed up, and how he at length took down his rifle, and went down the line of the critters still alive, and at the end fired the last bullet into his own head. The tale is not apocryphal.

I should perhaps add that in southern climes the role of a hard winter is taken by a prolonged drought, and so here too a carry-over of hay is equally valuable.

Therefore you will come, as your experience lengthens, to watch with ever-increasing satisfaction your stacks going up one by one, and when at length the last has been topped off, the hands paid off, the draft horses turned out to pasture,

the tractors backed up into the shed, each stack measured up
and fenced off, you will experience the lean contentment of
the old hymn writer:

> All is safely gathered in,
> Ere the winter's storms begin.

# VII.  The Horse

The cow horse has the status on a ranch of a working partner, and is given the respect to which his accomplishments—or promise—entitle him. An intelligent, experienced, willing cow pony never carries a price tag in range country, unless his owner is in the throes of adversity. It is nearly impossible, therefore, to buy a good herse from a going ranch; the cowpuncher on daily wages, however, is not characterized by great providence, and sometimes gets into a plight where he has to put up his mount for sale. There are also in most ranching districts horsemen who breed and break out horses as a business, and not infrequently the beginner can arrange to purchase his mount from such a place. The majority of horse breeders, being in the business, will fairly represent their wares, which cannot be said of the itinerant horse trader, of whom it is well to beware.

Later, as one becomes established, the breeding of light horses can be taken on, and there is no department of ranching that offers as much interest—or as much assorted grief. The selection, training, and care of saddle horses is something that, once begun, you will never voluntarily lay down. It is strongly flavored with the element of speculation, for even under the best conditions you will suffer disappointment. But even so the majority of ranchers who run a string of light horses as a side line find justification in the occasional top horse that they turn out, and there is a strong element of pleasure in just watching each clean-limbed colt as it develops, for each of these, as it comes two years af age, is, in its inscrutable promise, not unlike a budding young girl.

The role of the horse on a ranch is of such a nature that I have earlier designated your capacity for handling—or your ability to learn to handle—horses as one of the three touchstones of adaptability to a ranching career.

The eastern riding academies and stables may well furnish a valuable store of experience. Fundamentally the nature of the horse, like that of humankind, is pretty much the same east or west, or perhaps I should say that east or west it is uniform in its diversity. But western environment and the nature of the work performed make for many profound modifications. The horse in the East is now largely a means of entertainment and recreation. He may be equally such on a ranch; he is also not only a tool of production there but, as I have said, a working partner.

The difference between eastern and western riding I have often thought of as that between yachting and deep-sea fishing. The yachtsman generally has as his purpose the winning of a race, and after this is over he snugs down his craft and pulls a tarpaulin over the cockpit and goes home. He may acquire much of the lore of the art of sailing, and a smartness and dexterity greater than that of the blue-water fisherman. His boat is likely to be more nicely rigged and better painted, narrower of beam and easier of counter, than the fisherman's yawl or schooner that is berthed alongside. But if I had to make my living from the sea I think that I would take the boat and the companionship of the professional.

The cow pony has something of the fishing boat's lines, and the Thoroughbred those of the yacht. The western horse has to have a generous barrel, for when the day's work is over he recoups his energies by grazing all night, and grass is a bulky feed. He carries a forty-pound saddle plus his rider over rougher country and for longer hours than his eastern cousin, and therefore has to be closer coupled—you may remember from physics that the deflection of a beam is a function both of the load put upon it and of its span. Since his country is in general hillier, he has to have more powerful quarters, in order both to spring up the hillsides and to brake going down. There is, I might explain, no linkage in the horse's shoulder blades that permits of strong braking action. The cow pony also is taught to turn on his hind feet, and this again demands strong quarters.

The typical cow horse then is somewhat closer coupled and chunkier than the eastern hunter. In weight he can range upwards to eleven hundred and fifty pounds. He should have a small head, not too narrow a muzzle, a bright eye, a neck not too long, medium-high withers, a fairly easy shoulder line, a deep chest well muscled, straight forelegs set not too far apart, a good spring of ribs, a well-filled croup, and strong quarters. His underpinning, fore and hind, can be judged by the same standards as that of the riding academy, except that a heavier bone than that of the Thoroughbred cannot be counted a fault. Pasterns should be easy for the rider's comfort, and of course it is true the world over that "no hoof no horse."

As to judging performance after conformation has been scored, there is a standard set of maneuvers that correspond to the paces through which the eastern horse is put on tanbark or track. The cow pony can be tried out for speed, turning, at cutting cattle, and at roping. But the rating is by no means complete even then, for you have to find out about the two attributes that in the aggregate outweigh all others, which are disposition and sure-footedness. You won't live long to enjoy the flashiest and best-molded horse if he can't keep his feet under him on mountainside or badger-holed prairie.

The chances are that you will not know much about these two attributes until you have ridden the horse a matter of a week, in the actual process of working cattle. If he proves out then, the final stamp of approval can be put upon him. As an old-timer once put it to me:

"You set and look at a horse—at all his points. You mark him down in your mind from muzzle to croup. Then you get on him and touch your spurs to him and throw the score card over your shoulder."

Thus it is that you will seldom find the role of top horse in any rancher's string filled by the best-looking animal. It may be indeed some horse far down the line in looks, but you can be sure that the pony thus honored is intelligent and sure-footed and lifey.

In the matter of intelligence, let us consider for a moment what the all-around cow horse has to learn in order to qualify for the job. He should be able to cut a critter quietly, expertly, from the bunch, moving in behind it and turning as it turns, working it slowly out of the herd. In this process the rider should not have to guide it by rein or weight, for a good cut horse should not require more than to have the selected critter indicated to it. And once out of the bunch the pace quickens, for the critter, finding itself alone, tries to get back. This the horse prevents by anticipating every move, dodging and turning on a dime, and his rider has to have a firm seat to stay in the game.

This same instinct to anticipate the critter makes a horse good on the cattle drive. Driving a string of cattle is a good deal like pushing on the end of a rope—the push cannot be too quick or too strong, and must be applied at just the right moment. Therefore, when you notice a compact bunch of cattle being trailed across some bald prairie, taking an arrow-flight course for an unseen objective, you can wager that there are good horses and good riders on point, wing, and drag.

The good cow pony must know the roping game—just where to put his rider at a dead run when the loop is circling his head and, when the split second has come, when to pull up in a dead stop. The green or jug-headed horse will want to stop when the loop has left the roper's hand. This is wrong; the pull-up should come when the noose is at the end of the throw.

The cow horse must know how to hold a critter at the end of the rope, by facing it and moving around with it when the rider takes his dallies around the horn and dismounts. He should know that it is fatal to give slack at any time, and yet he should not pull back so hard as to strangle the critter.

I think that it will be conceded that the foregoing all adds up to the requirement that the finished cow horse know just about as much of the nature of cattle as the owner himself, and the surprising thing is that there are on western ranches so many that can thus qualify. Not all have the various jobs down with equal perfection; some will be better at one than another. The horses that are finished performers soon become known near and far, and reflect glory on their owner. There is a saying: "With that horse on the ranch all you have to do is to make out the deposit slips."

Besides the lore pertaining strictly to cattle, the cow pony must also have stored in his head a lot of miscellaneous knowledge for instant use when the right occasion arises, such as that if he gets into a snarl of barbed wire he should stand stock-still until his owner extricates him (this comes hard and many horses never learn it and get cut up as a result). He should know how to handle his feet when fording a stream, and how to go through a mudhole and not get bogged down, and where on icy going he can keep his footing and where he cannot, and how to dodge a badger hole at a lope. He should stand "tied to the ground," i.e., immobile when his reins are dropped.

It is almost impossible for a horse to acquire the sure-footedness necessary to a long life in the West unless he acquires it by instinct from running native pastures or range with his dam. It is very unwise to turn out a purchased eastern registered stallion or brood mare with a bunch of the natives. Any strange horse will of course have to run the gantlet of initiation into the group, and this, horses being more cliquey than a bunch of Colonial Dames, is in itself a hazard, and when a horse that is being hazed around by the others doesn't know how to keep his feet at a run, disaster is liable to follow.

In addition to sure-footedness, the horse that is native-foaled acquires the knowledge of how to protect himself against the many dangers that will beset him all his life. In this process his wits are sharpened and he is conditioned to receiving the multiple lessons that are crowded upon him when he comes of working age. His range birth confers the same advantage over his stabled and hand-fed cousin that the urchin from the city streets has over the boy from the mansion uptown.

And yet all this fund of native wisdom is not infrequently inadequate to preserve him through the many hazards. The variety of accidents that can happen to a horse on the range is almost inconceivable. There are the wire cuts that I have mentioned. Lightning not infrequently kills. Poisoning from toxic weeds, while less frequent than in the case of cattle, does occur. If a horse in rolling gets on its back in a hollow, even a slight hollow, he cannot get out of it, and soon dies. Drownings happen; just last spring we lost one of the best cow ponies we ever had on the place, together with an unbroken three-year-old and a young draft team, from this cause. The four head had evidently ventured out on the rotten spring ice of a natural pond in order to pick over the reeds thatching a muskrat house, and the ice gave way under them and they could not break their way to the shore.

The disappointments are many in running or in raising horses, and they do not always come from such sudden losses as that described above; sometimes they come from the dawning consciousness that a likely-looking youngster just hasn't got it in him to make a cow pony. This is forced in upon you as you break him and work with him. When this happens the horse can be dealt with according to the degree of his incompetency. He can be used, if he is especially good-looking, for what the cowpuncher calls "a Sunday horse." Or he can be put at such menial tasks, in single harness, as the cultivation of the garden. Or he can be sold for fox meat. Do not make the mistake, as I once did, of trying to make him over, if he is really a knothead, but get rid of him. The most dangerous kind of mount is one that blows up in a crisis. Things can happen swiftly in western riding. You may be jogging along under a warm sun and a blue sky one moment, and the next find yourself on the ground wondering when they'll miss you at home and start a search.

There is a world of difference between a horse that blows up in a pinch, and one that unwinds when he feels too good. I myself would not care to ride a horse that did not have the spirit to pitch when just the right set of conditions comes along, such as when some fine morning he is saddled up after being run out on green grass for months, or when he has been driving a bunch of his pals out to pasture, and suddenly finds the gate being closed and himself on the wrong side. A horse so spiritless I would not want around, any more than I would want as a partner a man incapable of a sense of elation or triumph.

But I expect him to buck honestly, and not throw himself,

or rear over backwards. I once persisted in trying to break a very good-looking horse that was given to rearing and pawing the air. I had tried all the standard devices to cure him of this habit, such as throwing my weight forward, and hitting him between the ears with a quirt butt, and thought that I had made over what was essentially a knothead until one day I was driving a bunch of horses far from home, and had turned to leave them. It was early afternoon; the next thing I knew I was on the ground holding a splitting head, and it was twilight. The horse was dimly visible in a clump of brush, where he had got his reins tangled. I managed by great effort to get him, and mount, and make my way back home; there I spent a week in bed with what the doctor called a severe concussion just short of a fractured skull. This was the closest call I have had; for the rest my accidents have been limited to the usual broken ribs from not landing just right—except when I was once tempted to try the other man's game and, skiing in the near-by mountains, broke a leg.

There is thus a world of difference between good spirits leading to an occasional bucking or crowhopping spell, and real blowing up in a pinch. The nature of the pinch is often unpredictable, and usually happens when you are riding alone. You may be riding through some brush in a coulee, and a projecting stick rams itself between your foot and the stirrup. If the horse cannot be reined in then, but blows up and bucks, the least you can expect will be a broken leg. Or you have tied on to a calf and are holding it when a blethering steer runs into the rope, dragging it around and under the horse's crupper. If the horse really blows up then, the chances are that you will go down in a tangle of horse, rope, calf, and steer.

Or, you are riding along a mountain trail, and the forelegs or hind legs of the horse slip off when a stone comes out of its bed. The wise horse holds himself to good footing with his unencumbered legs, until his rider can go off over his head and help him with a pull on the reins. Or, a cinch can come loose while heading a critter on the run, and the saddle starts to turn, or a bear can appear around the bend of a trail, or any one of a thousand other things can happen.

Your fate then depends on what kind of horse you have under you. Even with the greatest care you cannot forfend against everything that can happen, and the wonder of it to me is that the cow-town hospitals, instead of having the fracture ward only comfortably full of cases labeled broken collarbone, or fractured leg, or fractured ribs, do not have every bed in the place occupied by stove-up cowpunchers, as indeed occasionally they do have when spring and fall gathering time happens to coincide with iced-up hillsides.

✾

The exciting moments and the sudden crises of which I have spoken are infrequent, and the companionship with your horse is in general a tranquil one, composed of long hours trailing cattle, or jogging through the pastures, or riding with the mail in winter when the roads are blocked. In such manner is spent a large part of your waking hours year in and year out, and having a good horse under you ranks next, perhaps, to having at home a cheerful and helpful wife.

Therefore, the most important gait of the cow horse is his walk, and this can be trained into the colt by assiduous attention. The quality described as being up on the bit also is important, so that all that will be necessary, even at day's end, to get your horse into a trot is a slight forward movement of the reins. You will ride western style, with slack lines, the guidance of your horse being done as much by the shifting of your weight as by the feel of the reins on his neck.

This style of riding with slack reins comes from the advisability of giving your horse his head at all times—especially when you are traveling at a gallop. His reactions and perceptions are much faster than yours, and he can be trusted to find the right way over rough ground. The four reins, snaffle and curb, of the eastern rider excite the amusement of the cowpuncher. Charley Russell once said that he had known many a man who could drive sixteen or twenty head of horses with fewer lines than the eastern park rider uses. He referred to the old jerk-line freighter.

And if you wear spurs you will not use them actually to rowel into the horse's flanks. The mere suggestion of bringing them into use should suffice; a cow pony that needs spurring on to do his work should be relegated to the school run.

The breaking of the colts on a ranch is an event attended with interest on the part of all hands. On the small or medium-sized ranch the horse bunch is not so large that its new arrivals cannot be identified and named almost from the time they are foaled. How each one will break out becomes the subject for many dinnertime conversations. The first year the foals will, after weaning, be kept around the buildings and halter broken and gentled. They will be fed during this crucial period of their growth—to stint the hay and oats then may condemn the colt to a stunted adulthood.

The old-time method, on the big outfits, was to let the colts run with their dams on the range until four years of age. They were then run in, snorty and wild eyed, and roped and snubbed down until all but choked into insensibility. For many a thirsty hour they were left tied up, and then they were saddled, sometimes blindfolded and sometimes with their feet tied. They were bitted and bridled, and then the bronc buster got into the saddle and the blind was taken off, and the fun began.

It was a rough-and-ready system; it broke the spirit of some horses and made others outlaws, but it had one merit, and that was that it did not make for spoiled and contemptuous brats—barn pets that would insist on telling their riders where to go and when to head for home.

The treat-'em-gentle, tell-'em-everything school of thought

that has too often replaced the method of the older horsemen errs on the other side. The colts should by all means be fed well and halter broken and taught to permit the trainer to pick up their feet, but they should not be made pets of nor allowed to nuzzle people for sugar lumps or carrots. Respect should at all times precede familiarity. The half fondling and half teasing of colts is a pretty sure way to make headstrong brutes later in life, the kind that can get their riders into real jackpots.

Great patience and an always equable disposition are necessary in breaking horses. Horses vary in intelligence and character just as much as human beings, and no two individuals can be treated exactly alike. Consistency of treatment is more important than any particular method. When you have turned out the colts as yearlings on grass, your subsequent attentions will, on a working ranch, not be many until they are three or four years of age and ready for the serious training that is to make them into working partners. When, however, you get them in from time to time, to look them over, you should handle each one just as you handled them during the process of halter breaking. Horses never forget a lesson, and the approach to the lesson gives them their signal to gentle down and pay attention.

When they are ready for the saddle, it is best to get them into a barn or shed, rather than to work them in the open corral. The roof overhead is a symbol of that protection and care for which they are to trade their work. They should be gently bitted in the stall with a snaffle bit, and rubbed over with the hands, and then blanketed, and finally, after several days, be saddled, lightly cinched. The saddle should remain on their backs for increasing periods, and the master should put his arms on the seat and gradually increase the pressure. At the same time the cinch can be tightened a little, until it is finally at riding tautness.

At length the time comes to swing up into the saddle. This should be done in the corral, where the colt is in familiar surroundings. If he swings away from you as you put your foot into the stirrup—always facing backwards with the reins gathered and one hand on the poll and the other on the horn—stop until he stands still, even though this takes a matter of days.

If the average cross-bred ranch horse has been handled as I have outlined, he will, in about two cases out of three, do no bucking this first time you are on his back. The third horse will buck and it will be up to you to ride him and prove yourself the master. It will not infrequently be this horse that makes you the best mount in the end.

It is after the horse has learned to carry you without protest that the many lessons in ranch work begin.

✧

My many hours in the saddle, persisting now for many a year, have afforded me a chance to speculate on the strength of the attachment of man for the horse, and its persistence under the advance of the machine age. This quality in the western stockman, working as he does with horses and being aided by them to make his living, is understandable, but I suppose that, scattered around the perimeters of our great cities, there are now fully as many saddle horses as there are on the ranches of the West. The owners of these horses work to support them rather than the reverse. Yet the desire to own horses persists with no diminishment, and the demand from the cities is such that we on the ranches sometimes have hard work to keep at home our promising young saddle stock.

It must stem from some strong and deeply ingrained characteristic of the horse that elicits the admiration of man, and I think that I can put my finger on it. It is man's inability through the centuries truly to conquer the spirit of the horse. He can break this spirit, but he cannot conquer it, and because this spirit is essentially noble and independent in nature, man wonders at it and is drawn to it.

The horse has learned the meaning of the rope, the bit, the saddle, and the corral; he has accepted the fact that man by their use has acquired a certain dominion over him, but he has never found it desirable to cringe or fawn under them. He cares nothing whether his master likes him or not, if he does not abuse him. He seems to know instinctively that if man were to vanish from the face of the earth he would resume on desert and plain the untrammeled freedom that he has, for a period, had to forgo. A Westerner, Will James, who writes well about the horse put it thus:

"What I like about a horse is how independent he naturally is."

This independence permits very little of the element of affection. By affection I do not mean recognition, for which it is often mistaken. In a long association with the horse, ranging from the northerly limit of his range to the tropics, and from the Atlantic to the Pacific, in such varied relationships as an artilleryman, a weekend park rider, a packer and prospector, and a rancher, I have seldom seen any evidence of affection by the horse for humankind. The exceptions to this have been in the case of children. The horse is activated in his relationship to man by just two motives, which are fear of punishment and hope of reward.

In this opinion I note, in thumbing over the definitive work *Breaking and Riding,* that I am supported by no less an authority than James Fillis, perhaps the greatest trainer of high school horses that ever lived.

This is not to say that the horse is governed only at short range by these two motives. He arrives, after being broken to saddle, at a working agreement with his master; he will not do those things which will evoke punishment unless some point of difference important enough to make the attempt worth while comes along. He will work cheerfully, up on the bit, in return for protection and care. But this does not mean affection; I have on a number of occasions seen a rider thrown, not by a bronc, but by his own regular mount, and momentarily knocked out, and I have never seen the horse show the slightest interest or concern in the fate of his master. This indifference is in contrast to the solicitude of the man's dog—in our brushy country we often ride with a dog—which invariably whines over his master and licks his hands or face.

❄

The Western bronco is by far the most interesting of the types of horses I have known. At the outset I should perhaps call attention to the confusing use of this term. Generically, in the equine world, this means the variety of horse descended from the original Spanish or Barb stock and now native to the western plains and deserts. "Bronco" is a Spanish term meaning rough or untamed, and is applied usually to animals but sometimes colloquially to persons. It is the opposite of "manso"—gentle, mild, tame. The Westerner sometimes uses "bronco" in this generic sense, but more often in the specific when referring to a particular unbroken animal, or to a string of unbroken animals.

There are of course various types of the native horse, distinguished chiefly by color although sometimes also by conformation, such as the appaloosa and buckskin and pinto. These three types predominate in the herds of the Indians, which are generally designated by the term "cayuse," although sometimes also by that of "nichi," which is a Cree word meaning "we the people." This, I am told, is as near as these aborigines can come to the term "Indian," in which quaint conceit we perhaps can afford to indulge them in view of the circumstances.

To designate the breeding of a horse, the Westerner often uses the terms "cold-blooded" and "hot-blooded," the former being applied to the native horse as it ran the prairies uncrossed with any extraneous breed. The term "hot-blooded" is reserved for the Thoroughbred, the Kentucky, the Standard bred, and other segregated breeds.

The ranchers that I am acquainted with now seldom use horses that are wholly cold-blooded. Certain of them use a definite outcrossing system, others merely select breeding stock that to the eye shows hot blood. By crossing these more refined breeds on to the western strain one can often secure an animal that has the toughness, sagacity, and endurance of the bronco and the docility, size, speed, and intelligence of the studbook strains. The combination of the two makes the present-day western cow pony, which I believe is better all around than his forerunners which used to fill the remudas and cavvies of the old range outfits.

In my opinion, however, the western strain should be kept dominant; that is, there should be more "cold" than "hot" blood. (For convenience the term "blood" is used although it is frowned upon by scientific breeders.) This does not necessarily mean that a half-Thoroughbred should be crossed on a native; many of the traits of the native are genetically dominant and this strain will predominate even where the sire or dam comes straight out of the studbook.

The usual manner of introducing hot blood into a horse herd is to breed native mares to registered sires; this is the system I have been following, using, through the generosity of a larger neighbor—the McIntyre Ranch—either a Thoroughbred or a Kentucky stallion, since my demands for saddle horses are not sufficient to justify keeping a registered sire.

In expressing the opinion that the present-day cow pony is a better all-around horse than his earlier ancestor, I wish to emphasize that the term "all-around" is used advisedly, for there was one respect in which the native horse could not be touched, and that was his endurance. There used to be a great deal of argument on this score and the advocates of the hot-blooded strains were very vocal. Not only, said these, were the eastern breeds swifter but, since they and their ancestors had been fed and tended for generations while the broncos had been left to rustle for themselves on the bleak and stormy plains, they would logically be expected to have the better staying powers.

There was at one time a strong economic incentive to the putting of the two strains to the test, in that the U.S. Remount Service which was buying hundreds of thousands of dollars of horseflesh each year would be strongly influenced in its choice.

The controversy, which had begun with the range cattle industry, had reached the boiling point by 1908. In June of that year the question was put to a spectacular test, in the form of a race of 600 miles, sponsored by the Denver *Post*. The course was set between Evanston, Wyoming, and Denver; it afforded a sample of every kind of western going, including a 60-mile traverse at the start of the so-called Green River desert, where the horses had to travel in sand to their fetlocks, and the crossing of the Continental Divide. A purse of the comparatively modest amount of $1,200, divided into six prizes, was raised. I find that little is known of this race, even in cattle country, and so perhaps a summary will be in order.

When the race was announced the field immediately became divided between the hotbloods and the coldbloods, and the two camps scoured the West for their fleetest horses and their toughest riders. Twenty-three horses were at the start on May 29th. The entrants included two cowpunchers who, not having the price of a train trip for themselves and their horses, rode sixty-five miles a day for four days and reached the starting point the day before the race. Both these broncs finished. Of the hotbloods starting, the Thoroughbred, Standard bred, Kentucky, Morgan, and Hambletonian were represented.

The bronc starters were on the light side in weight, averaging but 897 pounds. Their riders averaged with equipment 184 pounds. The other horses averaged 955 pounds.

For the first hundred miles the hotbloods showed well. The purse for the first horse crossing the hundred-mile mark was won by a Thoroughbred. After that the hotbloods began dropping out, and a peculiarity of theirs was that they gave out, not by degrees, falling farther and farther to the rear, but all of a sudden. One of the Thoroughbreds came in well up on the evening of the fourth day. His rider told a bronc owner that he would tell the boys in Denver that he had seen him. The bronc man sized up the Thoroughbred in a quick glance and said:

"If you are going to do that you'll have to wire it in."

The next day that Thoroughbred foundered on the trail.

On June 5th at four-thirty in the afternoon two broncs crossed the finish line at Denver in a dead heat. They were a bay named Teddy, weight 1,025 pounds, ridden by C. E. Workman, 161 pounds, of Cody, and Sam, a roan, weight 911, ridden by F. T. Wykert, 193 pounds.

Three more broncs finished between then and the official time limit at 9:20 P.M. the next day. Five more also finished. Of the ten horses that finished only one, in fifth place, had hot blood; he was listed as Hambletonian and bronc. One of the finishers was a 208-pound man on a bronc mare named Little Minnie, weight 722 pounds.

The race excited great interest at the time, and it was estimated that a crowd of fifty thousand people saw the parade of the winners in the streets of Denver the day after the finish. The leading citizens of the town proposed that the next year another race be run over the same course, and announced that they were prepared to put up this time a purse of ten thousand dollars, a very considerable sum in those days when the Brown Palace Hotel offered a five-course dinner for sixty cents. The civic authorities fell into line; the Quartermaster Corps of the army seconded the idea; the newspapers proposed supplemental prizes and honors— everything was prepared for an even bigger and better race, but there was one thing lacking, and all the plans finally came to naught. No hotblood owners could be found willing to enter their horses!

The average daily distance that these horses covered in this race was about 75 miles. The fact that this pace was kept up for eight consecutive days is extraordinary, but a 75-mile ride in a day in cow country does not call for special comment. It usually follows the delivery of cattle to some loading or distribution point, after which you and your horse get a craving for home pastures. He knows what is up even before you turn his head toward home pastures. Gone is the side-drifting and ear-swiveling animal of the morning of departure. His ears prick forward, and his gaze looks over beyond you as you mount. You settle yourself in the saddle for a long swift trip.

My pleasantest ride of the year comes after I and some of the neighbors have trailed our yearling heifers for three days, to their summer range. This lies well up in a mountain valley that twists around for a long distance before it finally debouches on a series of big flats, where we drop the cattle and make camp under the spring sky. The next morning we take our separate ways homeward; my horse and I know a short cut, and we sashay up over slide rock to a saddle above the valley. We then have three miles through the finest upland meadow that you can imagine, with tall Douglas fir sparsely scattered, as if planted by some landscape artist with an eye for the view that opens between them. This meadow holds a chain of mountain tarns, and the mimulus grows in masses along their banks, and the yellow avalanche lilies march up the gentle slopes, outlining where the last tongues of snow have lain.

When we get to the end of these meadows we hit an old prospector's trail that we know about, and we follow it downward through dense shade, for close-growing spruce and balsam have here replaced the scattered fir, and looking upward through their interlaced greenery one would think himself at the bottom of a green and tranquil sea, and the white plumes of the tall bear grass are like coral reefs.

This forest ends abruptly on a grassy slope, and this leads down to gentle foothills, and far away over their grassy crests we can see the distant cut-bank on our river's course that marks our goal. It lies some sixty miles away. The horse always picks up this landmark before I do, and communicates the news to me by some slight quickening of the muscles.

Nine or ten hours later we pull up at the barn corral. The horse is back in the pasture where he was foaled, and I unsaddle and kick off my chaps and rub down his back, and walk toward the house, where a plume of fragrant willow smoke curls above the chimney, in sign that I have been seen and that food and welcome await me.

It is small wonder, given this close association of mount and rider, that so much of the talk in cattle country revolves around the horse. There are famous sires to be discussed, of both former days and latter, and the merits of their progeny, and just how this one and that one nicked with the families into which he was bred, and the mystery of the descent of family traits. The great roping horses are talked about and the cutting horses, and the flat racers and stake racers at the rodeos. The great buckers come up, and how they got started on their careers—how some pitched when first they were saddled, and how others were started out when some sudden mischance arose, and once having learned their power they never afterward gave anyone a peaceful ride. And of buckers that can turn it on and off, i.e., that are peaceful until a touch of the spurs on a certain spot gives them their cue; of broncs that let children crawl all over them, but are volcanoes when forked by a man. Of such was the great Midnight, a product of our country, who was the only horse ever to disprove the old cowboy maxim:

> There ne'er was a horse that couldn't be rode.
> There ne'er was a rider that couldn't be throwed.

All such things, and more too, you will hear as your experience lengthens. Your first concern as a beginner will be with the critter and there will be time enough to get interested in the embroidery and refinements of horseflesh when you are somewhat established. Pending that time you can, as I have said, ride a gentle plug. But unless you are differently constituted than almost any man I ever knew who really took to the ranching life, it will be only a matter of time until you are drifting over to where a group of men are talking horse, and then you will be contributing your bit, and it will not be many years until you stop in the middle of a sentence when something real good in the way of horseflesh trots by.

I should like to close this chapter, which otherwise might go on forever—there really being no proper place to stop talking about the horse—with an anecdote about Tom S——, the foreman of the Bar Triangle outfit.

Tom was taken by a friend one evening to see the movie *Gone With the Wind.* He had to make a real effort to get to town, since the day was stormy; he rose extra early to see that the cattle were fed, and then rode eighteen miles through snowdrifts and took a bus another twenty.

You may remember something of the dramatic suspense and lush pageantry of that very popular spectacle; how at the end of the first part the heroine escapes from burning Atlanta in an old hack drawn by the last horse from the once-replete family stables, and how as she flees you see (in Technicolor) the flames mounting skyward and licking out at the pathetic vehicle. Then there follows an hour of drama less highly spiced, but showing the vindication of the dainty heroine's wit and courage.

When the two-hour performance came to its close Tom and his friend walked slowly and silently to the hotel. As they parted the friend's curiosity got the better of him.

"Well, Tom, how did you like it?"

"I was just trying to figure out how they got that horse past all them burning buildings."

# VIII.  Ranch Recreations

There are certain callings that command the loyalty of their followers to the extent that the leisure hours of those who make their living from them are devoted to doing more of the same thing and doing it more strenuously. The lumberjack, for instance, puts on birling or woodchopping contests, and the hard-rock miner drilling matches, and the farmer cornhusking championships. Ranching belongs to this class also; on their days off the men go, the younger as participants and the older as spectators, to the rodeos and stampedes.

This manner of spending their leisure hours betokens, I should say, a zest for their callings far in excess of the city classes. I have never heard of a bricklaying contest staged by the building trades, or of a public accountants' field day where sets of books are closed against time, and I have not run across a contest among bankers who, given identical financial statements, compete to see who can most affably say no to would-be borrowers.

Those who take part in the rodeos have little time for anything besides training themselves and their mounts for the different events. I speak now of the true amateurs of the game competing for the most part in the local affairs. The big commercialized rodeos attract a professional class of performers who do little else than follow the circuit; these attain the greater proficiency, but this advantage is to my mind offset by the close acquaintanceship that one has with the local boys.

There are probably few of those who will read this book who will try out as rodeo performers, and there is little that the printed word could do to help them even if they should. One would have difficulty in writing out instructions on how to ride a bronc, or how to bulldog a steer or rope a calf; such counsel as might be given would be in nature akin to the advice given to the shy young man who wrote in to the personal counselor in a ladies' magazine, complaining that he suffered acute embarrassment upon entering a crowded drawing room. The advice returned was: Cultivate an easy and graceful manner.

One does acquire on a ranch, however, the ability to judge the merits of the performers at a rodeo. Bronc riding is judged as much by form as by the ability to stay the limit, just as ski jumping is judged by form as well as distance. All ranching districts with which I am familiar put on rodeos in summer, and these offer strong attraction to the ranch people. The scene may be the weather-beaten structures of a local fair site, or a natural amphitheatre in the hills or at the bend of a river. In such meets one often sees events that are left out of the big commercialized shows, such as flat races for cow ponies under stock saddle, and Indian stake races. The distraction of midway shows or stage shows is absent.

The younger men on a ranch who are to take part in such rodeos do not, as I have said, have time for much else. The older men may help out in coaching, but this will not take much of their time, nor do the rodeos themselves. There remain a certain number of leisure hours, distributed throughout the ranching years—principally in the late fall and winter—to be spent in other pursuits.

One would think that the rancher living, as is often the case, in a region where the game and fish are abundant, would be an ardent hunter or fisherman. This does not, however, seem to follow. Of the ranchers living within a hundred-mile radius of us, I know of only one who would be considered in the class of ardent sportsman. I should say that four-fifths of the game and fish taken in our foothills is taken by the people from the small towns or by the grain farmers from the plains or the irrigation districts.

Our rivers have trout and Rocky Mountain whitefish, and

our hills both small game and big game, in the form of the mule deer and elk. A short distance away, in the mountains, there are bear, both grizzly and black, and mountain goat and bighorn sheep. Before I chose ranching as a career I keenly enjoyed hunting and fishing, and the abundance of wild life was a by no means negligible consideration in my choice of a location.

At the outset I did a lot of hunting and fishing, but as time went on the edge of my appetite became dulled, possibly by satiety. I now go hunting and fishing rather infrequently, although when I do get around to it I still enjoy the occasional day in the field. One or two such as the opening of the trout season and the opening day of the bird season now usually suffice. Big-game hunting I now take as incidental to the much riding that I have to do in the fall. I pack a rifle but the buck that I take it out for now is a young spikehorn, and I let the old monarchs go. As to provision for the table, there is nothing in the way of game (except for bighorn sheep) that compares in palatability with good grass-fat beef, and there is always plenty of that walking around in our pastures.

There is hardly a man, by the way, in the range country who will not stoutly maintain that the flavor of beef grown out on wild grass is superior to that of beef finished in the feed lot on expensive grains. This is the kind of beef that one usually gets in the cities; it may have the edge on grass beef in tenderness and, as the packers say, "it cuts white," i.e., the color of its suet is white and not yellowish as in range beef, but for subtlety of flavor this feed-lot beef is not in the same class with mature grass beef.

Time was in my hunting career when I thirsted for the life of any game animal that I would see walking the hills. Now, however, it is a thrill to watch, and let go unscathed, the big bucks, or the bull elk lording it over a sleek harem. It is a delight to see the great coveys of sharp-tailed grouse that in the autumn gather in the chokecherry brakes, and to watch the wild mallards gleaning the oat stubble, and the gray geese and the honkers grazing the new growth in the hay meadows.

There is, however, a kind of hunting in our country in which I and all my neighbors join with alacrity, and that happens when the grizzlies get too bold or a pack of wolves drifts down from the north. Not all ranching districts have to contend with this source of cattle loss; the majority of ranges are by now as innocent of the big carnivores as they are of the buffalo. Not so, however, ours, and we yield steady tribute to the bears and intermittent tribute to the timber wolves. We have to the north and west a vast wilderness of mountain peak and valley, from which at intervals there debouch these calculating and elusive killers. What occasions these incursions is obscure; one would think that they would coincide with the low points in the cycle of game animals, but such does not always seem to be the case.

The grizzlies we have always with us; they are, in terms of the public health officer, endemic in our country. The surplus numbers in the mountains seem to spill out into the foothills, and there make such shift as they can. The grizzlies of a mountain range divide up, by one means or another, the territory into monopolies. The individuals seem to keep quite constantly within their own bailiwicks, but their surplus, and presumably the older individuals who have lost their territory by ordeal of combat, have to go somewhere, and the only open territory is in the high foothills where the cattlemen run their herds in summer. A certain proportion of these bears, confronted with the choice of earning a living by digging out ground squirrels and marmots and tearing up rotten logs for ants and outrunning the fleet deer or of killing the docile and obese cattle, choose the easier course. The grizzly kills cattle expertly, neatly, by dashing onto the chosen victim —a cattle-killing grizzly soon becomes an excellent judge of beef—and getting one forepaw on the critter's rump and the other on its muzzle. A powerful, quick hug snaps the neck. The grizzly often does not eat where he kills, but drags the carcass to a secluded spot. In this he shows his vast strength. A 1,200-pound steer will be dragged uphill and through brush as far as a quarter mile from the spot where it is killed.

When therefore we turn out our cattle in the spring we expect, as a part of the game, a certain loss from the grizzlies. There are other sources of loss, such as from drowning, bogging down in soap holes, and disease. Of a total summer loss of about one and one-half per cent (on our Association's summer lease) we figure that about one-half goes to the grizzlies.

We have to accept this, and try to keep the loss down by

furnishing our stock rider with heavy traps and plenty of ammunition. He will perhaps kill one or two grizzlies in a summer. But in certain years he discovers more carcasses killed by bears than normal. He has other duties than hunting bear; he has to put out salt and to ride the north and west limits to keep the critters from drifting out of roundup range in the fall. He reports to the Association president, and the latter sends around word that a few extra riders are wanted for the bear. He usually does not have much trouble in getting recruits—stern duty takes precedence over such humdrum tasks as fencing. Then the hunt begins in real earnest. We ride long hours, and we watch the fresh kills in relays, and set deadfalls baited with hog—an ursine tidbit. These deadfalls are more properly crowding pens, for they do not have any set-trigger device to impale the bear—a grizzly would take any such that could be contrived as a flea-bite. They are made of logs, in the form of a V, with the unfortunate porker at the apex. Heavy bear traps, so stiff of spring that they must be set with a screw clamp, are staked out in the mouth of the deadfall, in such a way that the bear in reaching for the bait must step into one.

In such manner we wage war, and sooner or later we get the ascendency. There is a sense of elation in the hunt, mingled, I suspect in more cases than mine, with a tinge of regret when a grizzly is brought down. One of the most thrilling sights in nature is to see a big grizzly walking his range, the lord of creation, except for the biped with his reeking tube and iron shard. There is immense power in the massive shoulders, and supreme arrogance in the triangular flat head, in conformation so much like that of a rattlesnake. When you put your sights on him, aim for the point of the shoulder and be sure you hold true. A not inconsiderable number of men are still killed by grizzlies each year.

But when the monarch lies still in death, this fleeting regret of which I speak comes over the more perceptive of the victors. You are the interloper on his ancient range, the aggressor upon his immemorial way of life. If a few wizards in chemistry and metallurgy had not armed you superlatively, you would have fled from him as did the bravest of Flatheads or Blackfeet or Nez Perces.

The wolves come much more rarely, but are harder to cope with. They, like the grizzlies, seem to overflow from the distant wilderness. In our country there have been three such invasions—once during World War I, the second some ten years later, and the third in the summer of 1944. Between these times not a wolf was seen, nor any wolf sign. I was, I believe, the first to sound the alarm. I was riding one of our home pastures, into which the bear never come, and found a dead calf. Then in the next pasture there was another dead calf, hamstrung and partly eaten, and another scampering around with its tail snapped off.

Then the marauder's diet shifted to sheep; he went across the river where a large band is run and killed fifteen head in one night. He returned to our side, and began taking two or three a night from the small ranch flocks that certain of my neighbors keep for their own use. The sheep he did not kill he bit across the loin, wantonly, something that a bear never does. Whereas in the two previous incursions the wolves had been in packs of four or five, it was obvious this time from the sign that a single animal was doing the killing.

The countryside went armed, and we rode in the early morning and late at night. From other ranching districts came reports of other single wolves on the rampage. There were apparently three other of the brutes operating in areas about fifty miles apart, equally bold in coming near the ranch houses.

The first sight of our wolf was had by a twelve-year-old girl, who was driving her father's small flock of sheep home at night. She had paused to enjoy a view of the sunset, and on looking back saw the wolf, huge and coal black, sitting on his haunches contemplating the scene. With great pluck she stuck to her band and got them home safe. Then a bunch of sportsmen from town, who had come out to lend a hand, were sitting about a campfire near the bed-ground of the big sheep band across the river, telling each other hair-raising yarns. They looked up to see the wolf lending an attentive ear. There was a mad scramble for the shooting irons, and by the time these had been loaded the wolf had drifted away.

By this time the nights had got frosty, and our wolf took to howling at night—a spine-chilling deep chime. His favorite stand was on a hillock fifty yards from the house of my neighbor to the south. When it became pitch dark he would begin his dirge, and howl every fifteen minutes. For two nights a posse sat awake and listened, and at crack of dawn deployed, but saw nothing. Then the third morning they went out and saw the wolf, leisurely trotting out to the day's work. He seemed unalarmed, and was brought down at about sixty yards. His pelage was coal black, with a sprinkling of white guard hairs. He weighed one hundred and twenty pounds, was six feet from muzzle to tip of tail, and had paws about the span of a man's hand.

The three other wolves met death in similar fashion; they were apparently unacquainted with man, and when they encountered a human being paid but little attention. One of these three wolves—all black like the first—sat on his haunches while a rancher went back to the house for his rifle. Until they were shot each of these wolves had killed approximately fifteen hundred dollars' worth of livestock. Since the invasion we have all wondered where these tame beasts came from; the opinion most favored is that they drifted down the front range of the Rockies all the way from northern British Columbia, where a black breed of wolves is said to have its home. In the previous invasions, which were much more destructive, the wolves were very wary, ran in packs, and were of the usual gray color.

✿

Perhaps the reason why hunting for sport does not greatly appeal to ranchers is that it is a more or less solitary occupation and does not possess the attribute that a pastime should have of contrast to one's usual activity or state. There is a strong urge of a Sunday to see something of one's fellows, and so on that day there is much visiting back and forth. Once the morning chores are done, denim and gingham are doffed and store suits and print dresses come out of the closet. Barn stalls are cleared for the accommodation of visitors' mounts. Of late years, up until the advent of the war, the use of horseflesh for visiting was diminishing and cars took its place, but the line of male conversation did not, as far as I was able to discern, shift from the equine to the mechanical.

Ranch communities create much of their own amusement. I have spoken of the local rodeos, all of which end up in a dance, which lasts until the men have to leave for the hayfields. Many dances also are staged in the one- and two-room schoolhouses, sometimes preceded by that sterling country institution, the basket supper. In this the ladies bring, in great secrecy, their gaily trimmed and brimming baskets to the school. Each of these contains a lunch for two, done in the best aesthetic and culinary manner that the owner is capable of. It may be suspected that those of the maids are likely to surpass in quality those of the matrons.

When the supper hour has come, the auctioneer mounts the teacher's stand and brings out the baskets one by one. The proceeds are scheduled for some worthy local cause— either the school fund or for the relief of some burned-out family. The bidding starts, and the swains of the countryside vie with each other for the privilege of buying the baskets suspected of coming from the more favored local belles, since the high bidder becomes the partner for the evening of the fair provider, whose name is concealed beneath the wrappings. There is naturally a great deal of rivalry and much searching of feminine expressions as the bidding mounts in intensity. This is supposed to be blind, but a sly tip, the mere flicker of an eyelash, from a damsel to a favored suitor has not been unknown.

Then in the fall there are turkey shoots, at which one's prowess with a rifle can be demonstrated. And later, as the work eases up, there may be amateur theatricals. When we were new to the country we went to these somewhat inclined to scoff, but the quality of the performances soon overcame our skepticism, and it was a proud moment when we were at length invited to take part.

The play chosen on the occasion of our debut was *The Whole Town's Talking.* Some of you may remember this robust farce that, some years ago, was a stalwart of stock companies and amateur dramatic societies. It calls for a dainty ingénue and an intrepid young hero. Our schoolteacher ideally fitted the former role, and we had a promising prospect for the latter, in the person of a young Englishman who worked about the country, adventure-bent. He had a muscular build, a handsome face, and, best of all, a clear, well-modulated voice.

He eagerly accepted the role, and rehearsals began in our

one-room schoolhouse. A difficulty at once arose; our male lead was, it developed, not only painfully shy, but also deeply enamored of his opposite. In her presence he stammered, and his resonant voice was throttled to a coarse whisper, and he approached the clinches as though the ingénue were a case of eggs. The whole project was threatened with extinction. A cowpuncher was impressed into the part, but he squinted against the lights, and couldn't be kept sidewise to the footlights, which was necessary to conceal his widely bowed legs, upon which the eyes of the audience otherwise became fixed.

Somehow or other each ranching community seems able to provide someone with real coaching talent, and ours was no exception. Our coach, moreover, had ingenuity as well as talent. The Englishman was called back. Censure having failed—it only made him doubly shy—a dummy was contrived out of gunny sacks stuffed with hay, and this was taken out at night to a secluded spot and hung from the limb of a cottonwood. The coach took out the Englishman and told him to practice both his lines and his embraces on the dummy.

A week or so later he rode back to report to the coach that he had got pretty good with the dummy. A gray-haired matron was then impressed, and when he had again become fluent, her younger sister was put in. This third stage was not completed until the day before the dress rehearsal, and an anxious cast gathered to see whether the play could go on.

To the delight of all, the Englishman spoke with fervor and embraced with ardor.

The play was a great success, and was called for by other school districts, and finally by the townspeople. The town performance was the windup, and at the last curtain call the hero turned expectantly to his partner for the final accolade. She brought out from somewhere a large tin medal, inscribed so that all might read: CHAMPION BULLDOGGER.

✿

Such community enterprises as rodeos and dances and turkey shoots and amateur theatricals come at fairly long intervals, and do not occupy all of one's leisure hours. There are many Sundays when the roads are blocked by either rain or snow. One then has time for a certain amount of reading. One of the pleasures least anticipated when we took to a ranching life, but one that has proved most real, is that conferred by the printed word. One of the reasons may be that reading is sedentary in nature, and it is a pleasure after a busy week to sit down indoors. This is, however, minor. The principal reason seems to be that the printed word has taken on a vividness that, for my part, I had not experienced since my childhood. This makes reading a gratifying pursuit. Why this should be caused me many hours of unhurried speculation, which in the end led me to discern two causes.

The first of these is that on a ranch one brings to reading a mind that has not been hammered upon by the great mass of utilitarian words and paragraphs that one must peruse in the course of the week in the city, and so the mind is fresher to receive impressions. We do not have a daily paper, for instance, but get the news from broadcasts or from a weekly digest.

The second reason, more important than the first, is that on a farm or ranch the abundant metaphor of the more classic writers comes alive. This is because the reader shares the experiences upon which so many of these metaphors are based and from which they take their color. We now look not upon a photograph of a painting but upon the painting itself. It takes the prism of participation to bring out the spectrum of metaphor.

Let me illustrate what I mean by an example. In Act I of *Richard III* the Duke of Clarence is pleading in his cell with the hired murderers. He soon learns that no help can be expected from the king; he has another brother, Richard, who spoke kindly to him when he was seized. He begs the murderers to go to Richard, for Richard will not have him cut down. The murderers receive this cynically.

"*Clarence*. Oh, do not slander him, for he is kind.

*First Murderer*. Right—as a snow in harvest."

Now because I in common with almost every other farmer and rancher in this northern country had had a snow in harvest this simile breaks sharply, as sharply as a well-pitched curve. The scene can never be so vivid to the man who has not had a snow in harvest. When you yourself have selected, stored, tested, and treated the seed; when you have plowed, disked, harrowed, and drilled the fields; have perhaps irrigated them; have watched for hail the menacing thunderheads; have seen the ears swell, ripen, turn brown; are at last ready to cut the field, only to have a snowstorm break before you can start—then you know that Shakespeare chose the inevitable metaphor for this, the first great dramatic moment of the play. A lesser dramatist would have written: ". . . as a rain in harvest"—and got a weaker effect. A rain though annoying is but of small consequence, for the field dries when the sun comes out and the wind rises. The consequence of a snowstorm is lasting, for it lodges the standing grain so that it cannot be reaped, and much of it is irretrievably lost. All this, when you know, you get in an instantaneous mental scanning as the words unroll.

Or take a scene from another classic. The prophet Hosea is reproaching his people for their waywardness, and he exclaims:

"Israel slideth back as a backsliding heifer."

That is a very vivid metaphor. It is evident that Hosea had handled livestock, and the translators of the Authorized Version were close enough to the soil to let the metaphor stand. There is nothing in all creation as stubborn as a heifer—say a yearling heifer that has been roped out of the cowherd. No metaphor (I here use "metaphor" in its generic sense to include metaphor and simile) more apposite could possibly have been chosen. You see a wild-eyed critter, nose pointed up along the rope, firmly resolved to choke to death rather than move.

The Revised Version has *stubborn* in place of *backsliding*. Perhaps the translators here thought their word more elegant, but they lost in color.

Most of the world's great literature was written before the very recent advent of agricultural implements, and thus at a time when agriculture furnished the livelihood not, as at present, of a decided minority of the population, but of the great majority. What was then a general manner of living has now become a specialized and segregated manner. To everyone then a metaphor based on agriculture was a live metaphor, and thus it made alive its context.

The grandest metaphor in all the written word was couched in the terms of this calling: "Whatsoever a man soweth, that shall he also reap." This is one that the rancher might well think upon when the tedium of the many tasks—the branding, the fencing, the haying—that must intervene between the rare gatherings of his beef begins to oppress his spirit.

There were in those early days two lesser sources of metaphor, and both of these have also now faded with the first. These other two are the institution of royalty and the sea. Now under the stimulus of modern invention we find metaphors taken from literally hundreds of trades and callings, and in the nature of things only a few of these can be alive to any one reader. Most of these and the callings from which they stem do not, to the rural reader (to use an abhorrent but current metaphor) register. Nor do the ironic or satiric moods in which so many modern books are written register. What he is looking for is something sentimental like the wedding scene in *Lorna Doone,* or Henry Esmond at his mother's grave, or the convalescence of the Virginian after the Indians have shot him, or something humorous like Falstaff in a clothes hamper or Mr. Pickwick shooting daws, or something exciting like the chariot race in *Ben Hur.*

✿

We shall have to grant the rural reader his particular kind of literary taste, whether it conforms to the modern trend or no, and I hope that the critics will not be too censorious of his retreat from reality.

In cattle country there is after all a great deal more palavering done than reading, and the subject should not bulk large. But one deals with metaphor in the spoken word as well as the written, and here I pause to view with regret the displacement of good western idiom by the cheaper coinage of the mechanical and commercial trades. Of all the brands of English spoken the world over, I know of none so apt, humorous, and terse as that developed and spoken in the old West. It is admirably suited both to the country and to the trades of that country, and it should not be allowed to pass, by the process of gradual dilution, into the limbo of the lost. Its metaphors were derived from three main sources—ranching, placer mining, and poker. Taken together these trades furnished the livelihood of the overwhelming majority of the sparse population of the old West.

What launched me upon this line of thought was the chance remark of one of my companions the other day, wherein this submergence of native speech first struck me forcefully. I had been driving cattle through the pasture of a neighbor. His son, a youth of about twenty years of age, came out to lend a hand. He did it competently and when we had finished and had had our smokes he unhooked a leg from his saddle horn and turned to go.

"Well," he said, "I've got to be stepping on it."

What his father would have said, or indeed any other of the earlier generation, would have been: "I've got to be high-tailing it." That westernism has as its basis the habit of calves, when startled into a run, of raising their tails ramrod-stiff as they scamper off. It means real speed, as one knows who has had to rope a calf on the run. Such a one sees the image when the metaphor is used. Contrast the connotation of "stepping on it." In its place it may be a good metaphor, but to me and my contemporaries it savors of burnt fuel and hot rubber and the clashing of gears. This youngster had often worked cattle, but apparently the mechanical metaphor had the greater power to impress. The boy belongs to the era of machinery; he had been brought into the world by our country doctor, who had, just the year before, traded in his buckboard for a Model T, and when the boy had saved his first hundred dollars he had at once put it into a secondhand car.

This boy had probably dropped from his lexicon a metaphor kindred to "hightailing it"—that of "afoot." This is as western as rimrock; it is redolent of saddle leather and sweet, clean-limbed horseflesh. It expresses exigent and immediate need. For example, during the worst of last winter's snow, a rider, living alone in a cabin across the Belly River, rode up to my door and said that he was plumb afoot for tobacco. In consequence, I gladly shared my store with him. A man can be afoot for a drink, for money, for companionship, or anything else. He can literally be afoot—bucked off on the range or put afoot by the lameness of his horse. It is no longer a serious matter, with a car at hand at the ranch house to be dispatched for him when he fails to turn up. Formerly it was not so; to be afoot meant actual distress, as I learned myself when, fresh to the country, I permitted myself to be bucked off many miles from home, and had to trudge in boots, packing chaps and spurs and coat, a vast distance over stony ridges, over slippery grass, across brushy coulees, and through prairie-dog towns.

Perhaps the most expressive use of the metaphor was recounted by my wife, when I showed her the opening paragraphs of this chapter. At one of our crowded schoolhouse dances the wife of a neighbor was enviously watching our popular and lissom schoolteacher, flushed and happy, cut in upon at every round, obviously the belle of the ball. This neighbor's wife had been perfunctorily danced with by her husband and his friends, who, the duty performed, had adjourned to the schoolhouse steps for a smoke and a powwow. In the intervals of soothing a fretful child, one of many disposed upon or under the benches of the cloakroom, she commented:

"I was all set to be a teacher; I'd had one year at normal school, and my uncle was school trustee in town, but Tom was coming over regular, every evening, and he was so plumb afoot for me that I just couldn't refuse him."

There is the man who *gets on the prod*. Such a one has become stubborn and unreasonable, or is acting in blind anger. A critter is said to be *on the prod* when, usually as the result of being handled unskillfully, or handled too much, it charges the horseman with rolling eye and foam-flecked muzzle. And there is the man who, by reason of too long a period of solitary or frugal living, *turns his wolf loose* when he hits town.

There are, of course, many words in western idiom that do not have such overtones of humor or distress as the foregoing. Such words may be borrowed from the Spanish (fertile source of westernisms, particularly on southern ranges), or from the French, or coined, or transferred from normal use and given an especial application. Examples of the first class are: *loco* from the Spanish word meaning crazy, *to palaver* from *palabra*, *hoosegow* from *juzgado*. Of those derived from the French we have: *coulee* meaning the bed of an intermittent stream (*vide arroyo*), *butte* (a hill), and to *sashay* meaning to switch-back up or down a hillside from *chasser*. Of coined words examples are: the *tackaberry* designating the quick-release buckle on the cinch latigo, and *brockle* meaning spotted when applied to the face of a critter. Examples of the fourth class are: *to wrestle* (always pronounced *wrastle*) meaning to throw down a calf preparatory to branding, *to pack* meaning to carry, *to haze* meaning to drive along, and *drugged* as past participle of the verb "to drag"—the unfortunate rider who on falling off his horse gets his foot caught in the stirrup is spoken of as being "drugged to death," and no Westerner on hearing this term ever thinks of a miscalculation on the part of apothecary or physician.

Although ranching people are wont to use more terms derived from their own trade than from those other two— placer mining and poker—that I have cited as making up in large part western idiom, they nevertheless fall into these also upon occasion. Few of the old-timers confined themselves exclusively to cattle; they drifted into mining and out again, and most of the men played poker. Thus, for instance, the metaphor of *getting down to bedrock* has more than a conventional meaning; not a few Westerners have literally with pick and shovel got down to bedrock, with the aureate gleam of bedrock treasure in the mind's eye. Some have known what it is to make a *cleanup* when their claim has *panned out*. You may remember that Owen Wister in *The Virginian*, one of the few books of western fiction where the idiom is used (although sparsely) correctly, makes his hero describe the play of *King Henry IV* as bedrock. You can rely upon a man of whom it is said "he *assays* up well." There is a strong element of finality to the decision of a man who *pulls stakes,* for when a miner pulls up the location stakes of his claim he has renounced all future interest in it.

To the third source of western metaphor—poker—a fair share of the credit for its vigor must be credited. As an enricher of the tongue poker ranks high; it is doubtful whether its supplanter, bridge, can ever touch it in this respect. In fact, not a single bridge metaphor that can stand on its own feet comes to mind. In contrast consider such stalwarts as *call you* and *stand pat* and *an ace in the hole* and *fourflusher.*

The Westerner most habile in the use of the language of poker that I have known was, oddly enough, a woman. I shall call her Malapy Meg. She was the sole inhabitant of an abandoned placer gulch up in the mountains, living in the only standing habitation, a one-room cabin bequeathed her by her last gambler consort, who, following the example of two predecessors in favor, had decamped when luck turned against him. Meg at first took his departure philosophically; experience had taught her that another would soon be along. But at length experience proved a false prophet; the gulch was so nearly worked out that no professional ever again appeared. Meg, after a period of discouragement, had at length reconciled herself to solitude and made a precarious living by growing vegetables with irrigation water supplied by a disused miner's flume. For many years she was shunned in orthodox manner—none of her unions having been, it was reputed, with benefit of clergy—but at length, after certain of the ranchers' wives had accepted some of the small services that were ever being prompted by her generous heart, she gained a slight footing in the community; this with the passage of time finally became complete acceptance. Thus when the daughter of one of the substantial ranchers in the district was married Meg was there to lend a hand. The bridegroom was a local boy, a top-notch cow hand of whom everyone approved. Meg was first in line to congratulate the bride:

"Honey, I drawed three cards and never filled. Here you get a pat hand that couldn't be beat in the state."

The third quality which I have said lends interest to western speech is that of terseness. One might think that the sparseness of population in the old West would have developed in the speech of its inhabitants the opposite quality; that the deprivation of neighborly intercourse would have opened when reunion at length took place the floodgates of speech. This, however, was not the case; in general speech was laconic. I suppose that, for one thing, the habit of solitary days and weeks was not easily thrown off; for another, there was (and still is) a scrupulous desire not to give offense where no offense is meant, the nature of the life tending to develop the qualities of quick decision and instant action. The old West held a not inconsiderable number of men who would rather be dead lions than living dogs.

This compression of utterance, this sententiousness, does not, I am glad to say, appear to be in danger of disappearance. I was discussing with a neighbor in the early days of the New Deal the many measures that were being taken to correct our maladjustments and to amend our ways and to reform our thinking.

"I reckon," he said, "that they mean well enough in Washington but they always get too much hay down."

He referred, of course, to the tendency of every beginner, and indeed of the incorrigibly impetuous, to mow more hay than can be properly raked, gathered, and stacked.

When offense was intended to be given, it could be done succinctly. The top hand of a large ranch had been given leave to ride in the rodeo circuit. He placed well up in the various meetings, and returned with a high opinion of himself. At the end of the first week back on the job he came to the owner and said that he figured that he was worth a whole lot more than he was getting. The owner looked him over from sombrero to spurs, very deliberately, and allowed a minute to go by. Finally he said in a disarming tone:

"Arthur, I guess you've growed into a real buckeroo. Yessir! But, Arthur, did you ever stop to think what this outfit would do if you should die?"

The question took Arthur aback; he stammered for a few minutes, and then answered hesitantly:

"Why, I reckon, I reckon—that is, you'd have to get someone else!"

"Arthur, you said it. Consider yourself dead."

✿

I find myself guilty again of a large digression from the subject in hand. But the chief source of recreation on a ranch does not lie in a planned program, either active or passive, but from following when time permits some impulse or some vagary of the mind. When you pick up and go to the nearest city the lights of street and shop shine more brightly for you than for the city dweller; the bustling in the streets, and the crowded hotel lobby, and the ordering from a menu, and the privilege of turning on the steam in your room—all are invested with a kind of childish fascination. You know that much of it is meretricious, and all of it evanescent, but you enjoy it hugely, until all of a sudden, perhaps with a clear sunrise or a warm wind from the prairie, it palls, and you head back.

The tasks themselves often hold the elements of recreation, when you take them properly. I have spoken of the effect of a quick glance into the waters of our river, or of a brief rest upon its banks. This is recreation in the literal meaning of the term; it can be had also when the rider reins in on a hilltop and looks over the land below him. He gets it when he looks up for a minute to see the thunderheads gathering over the mountains, or when riding alone in the evening he watches as the mountains take on a red glow from the sunset, and then darken into purple and at length into solid black, so that the range becomes at length a long silhouette of cardboard that has been cut out and pasted against the western sky.

On our range it comes in winter when it is most needed,

in the form of a chinook. This is the beneficent warm wind that ends our cold spells. Bitter cold is hard on men and beasts. The cattle get humps in their backs, and move disconsolately about on their feed ground, and a fresh snowfall melts into icicles that hang from their backs and rattle as they walk, and they low their discontent. Their appetite for the precious hoard of hay is enormous, and you make many trips with your sleigh between stack and feed ground, and an hour after you leave them the cattle are walking around hungrily looking for more. The horses get rime on their necks and chests, and their coats take on the luster of deep-piled plush.

The water holes freeze up and you spend many weary hours chopping them out (for it is even more important in winter than in summer to have water before the cattle at all times). The outflow of the springs freezes layer on layer, until the source of the water comes to lie at the center of a flat cone the sides of which are so slippery that the cattle cannot approach. The sun dogs, one ahead and one behind, march with their master across the southern sky, and as frosty night follows frosty night the stars get harder and brighter until at length they seem to hang right above the roof ridge, and the coyotes howl their maniacal glee, knowing that such weather puts the weaklings in their power.

The effect of such a cold spell is as though the whole country were put under the plate of a gigantic screw press, concave like the bowl of the sky; as the frozen dawns follow each other the press is turned down tighter and tighter on the range, until the pressure becomes almost intolerable.

Then one morning as you drive out to feed you glance at the mountain crests and see that they are smoking, and that the smoke plumes trail out toward you. Your heart leaps up; this is the forerunner of the chinook. It is still icy cold, but you know that relief is coming. You watch the mountain slopes at timberline, and see them take on a deep-green hue as the rising wind shakes the snow from the boughs of the spruce and balsam. You turn to look at the east, and see that the banners of the clouds are forming.

When you have got out to the cattle you know at once that they have sensed the change. They now call full-voiced, and they mill around the sleigh, and have the spirit to butt at each other. The chinook arch of clouds in the east has now taken definite form, and stretches from horizon to horizon, its leading edge tattered by the high winds. To the east of this arch the clouds are now solid gray, and to the west the sky is a dazzling blue.

It is still below zero, but now you can hear the wind roaring like distant surf, and from the vantage of your load you can see the tongues of dark woods on the lower mountain slopes where the warm winds, cascading downward, have first hit the ground.

And then all of a sudden the chinook hits the ranch. The effect is instantaneous, as if the door of a large oven were opened or as if an industrial unit heater were turned on.

There is no gradualness in it—trust the West to see to that. Within a matter of minutes the mercury climbs forty degrees. You strip off your outer garments; the tenseness within you relaxes; the screw of the cider press is backed out and the country comes alive again. Within an hour the snow has gone from the top of the hillocks, and within a day from the swales between, and the cattle leave their hay and graze hungrily the good bunch grass. The horse herd seeks out some hilltop and there dozes in the warm wind. There is at first little melting, for the wind is very dry and evaporates the snow rather than melts it; as the chinook persists, however, the water begins to run and each coulee has its rivulet that you hear tinkling as you ride by.

The chinook makes thousands of square miles on the eastern slope of the Rockies available for ranching by uncovering the grass and warming the cattle up so that their feed intake is reduced within economical limits. This famous wind is not, as so many believe, a warm wind coming from the Japan Current. Just a few miles to the west of the foothill belt it is icy cold; I have been in the high mountains in winter and have seen it thus. Its heat is imparted to it mechanically; as it flows down across the mountain crests it becomes denser, and the phenomenon of adiabatic compression takes place. An example of this is the generation of heat when you pump up a tire with a hand pump. The adiabatic gradient for a column of air insulated from external influences is about 1.6 degrees F. for each three hundred feet it falls. The chinook is the same kind of wind as the Föhn of the Alps or the harmattan of the Atlas Mountains. In the case of the former it is, like our chinook, benevolent, but in the latter, the country being plenty hot enough already, the wind is a curse.

Our chinook is so beneficent, so great an alleviator of our winter troubles, that I have known ranchers to name their daughters after it. What we think of it can perhaps be in some degree suggested by the answer that a cattleman of our country returned to a questionnaire. This man had achieved distinction in breeding registered Herefords and his college proposed to include him in some kind of honor roll of its alumni. They sent him a form on which was this question: Favorite recreation?

He answered: Peeling off in a chinook.

# IX.  Ranch Economics

It is as difficult to be specific about the profitability of the family-sized ranch as about the family-sized grocery store, or bakeshop, or any other commercial venture of the sort. There are so many variables in appraising the productivity and profitability of a ranch that about all one can do in writing on the subject is to apply the doctrine of limits. That is, it is possible only to define the limiting conditions—of over-investment or underinvestment, of understocking or overstocking, of being too casual or too painstaking—within which the area of profitability can lie.

From time to time I have had something to say about what constitutes ranching country. I have said that it is country that is too dry or too rough for the plow. The days are gone when the beginner could drift in and throw his herd onto such productive areas as the Red River Valley, or the Missouri

River bottoms, or the Judith Basin. These have rightly been taken over by the farmer. His intensive cultivation, bringing in its train schools and roads and towns, has raised the level of prices and taxes too high for the grazier. On land that is humid and fertile and flat there must be a greater yield per acre than that afforded by the natural grass cover, and so the grass is turned under. Feed grains and cereal grains, tame hay, canning crops, sugar beets, and all the rest have, in conjunction with the great increase in population, pushed westward and northward the herds of the cattleman. In not a few regions the farmer, to his perplexity and sorrow, has pushed the cattleman back too far, but in general the division of the land into its most economical uses (heavily subsidized irrigation districts apart) has now reached, by the process of cut and try, a state of equilibrium.

The line of demarcation between range and grange is often given as the 100th meridian, but this is a very inexact boundary, with many areas of grazing land lying, as in Texas to the east, and many productive farming regions lying, somewhat like islands in a vast sea, to the west.

The retreat of the cattleman began not, as most students of ranch economics would say, at the Missouri, but at our eastern seaboard. In the southern colonies there existed before the Revolution the prototypes of our western ranches. To quote from Sanford:*

* From *The Story of Agriculture in the United States*, by A. H. Sanford, published by D. C. Heath and Co.

There were annual round-ups and branding of calves, conflicts between overlapping interests, and long drives of herds to tidewater markets. Cattle rustlers plied their trade, and were summarily dealt with when caught. Might was the law of the range then, as later. These cattlemen, ever alert, always armed, fearless, resourceful, were an effective protection to the tide-water planters against attacks from the Indians of the Mississippi region. Those interested in the history of the cattle ranges of the Great Plains will find its beginnings in the colonial times in the South as well as in the Spanish ranches of the Southwest.

The cattle on these early ranches were of the longhorn type and not greatly different from those driven on to the western ranges two centuries later.

After the Louisiana Purchase the hardy Americans of the old Southwest—Tennessee, Kentucky, and Indiana—soon infiltrated into the territory of the Mexican hacendados and into the country of the Plains Indians. They quickly learned the rules of the game, and took over, because of greater numbers and greater industry, both the range of the hacendados and the hunting grounds of the buffalo eaters. The latter did not, contrary to popular opinion, resist very actively this invasion in the earliest years. The Indians were perhaps too bemused by the idiocy of men who (as an old Sioux chief is supposed to have said) killed off the animals that could care for themselves in order to replace them with animals that had to be cared for. When it became evident that the folly of the white man had no limits, they struck, but too late.

And in turn these same men, or their descendants, have been pushed northward and westward by the slow-moving, methodical, patient man in bib overalls, to whom a cow was something that was herded into a barn at night and milked. This retribution for the range man's rapacity continued slowly, inexorably, until the use of the land has, as I have said, reached a state of equilibrium.

As a matter of fact, the presence of farming areas, and in particular of irrigation districts, within and about the ranching areas is beneficial rather than harmful to the cattleman of the present day. His culture and that of the farmer supplement each other. He can sometimes buy feed from the farmer when his own supply runs short, or he can rent the farmer's fields for wintering his cattle, and in many instances he can sell his feeder steers to the farmer for finishing on beet pulp, corn, barley, and oats.

The presence of farms and farmers can, however, beguile the beginner into paying too high a price for his land. He can buy too close in to such districts, where the price of land is up on stilts because of association. The rancher will want some hay land and some land that can be broken and farmed, but as to the former he can get it in one or more of the natural hay meadows that lie along the courses of western streams like beads strung on a necklace, and as to the latter he can afford, where the straight farmer cannot, to break small rolling pieces of land because this sort of work is subsidiary to his main effort.

Although he can pay too much for his land, he can also pay too little or, rather, find that what seemed to be a bargain was in reality a swindle. It is perhaps well at this point, since land values lie at the base of ranching economics, to discuss what should determine the value of the land, and what the man launching into the business should pay for it.

For pay for his land he must; it is almost impossible to start out now except by buying into the game. What little land remains to be homesteaded is too poor in quality to repay the effort, and one homestead, either livestock or farming, is not now sufficient for starting a cattle outfit.

It is regrettable that the spirit of enterprise alone will not suffice, as in the old days; then many a farsighted cowpuncher quit riding for wages to locate on some remote piece of bottom land that he had spied on the roundup. There he erected a log cabin with a dirt or puncheon floor, built a pole corral, and started out. His string of culls would seldom fail to have twins each year, which was not too violently resisted by his range neighbors unless, as Charlie Russell said, his bulls started having twins too.

It was, however, no assurance of ultimate success to have started out in the early days. Not a few of the locators, with the whole country to select from, chose unwisely, preferring some hillside or shallow-soiled prairie to the bottom land. Nor were all of them adaptable enough to change with changing methods, and continued to turn out the race-horse type of steer until in some year of depression these became all but unsalable, and then the old-timer had to sell out his land. Not all the old-timers fared thus badly—many of them achieved solid comfort and a few affluence, but enough muffed their chance to constitute a parallel with the inventors and early pioneers in some new industrial field, who, although in on the ground floor, failed to get their economic bearings.

The amount of capital you will need at the outset does not have to be large; I have seen men do wonders on an initial stake of two or three thousand dollars. These brought to the business a precise knowledge of what they wanted, and they lived frugally, judged even by back-country standards. They also brought the quality of enthusiasm, either for the life itself or for the chance to be their own boss.

It should be recognized, however, that the economics of ranching, as contrasted with those of farming, entail a larger amount of capital in proportion to the gross value of the output, because both land and cattle must be purchased at the outset. The farmer need buy only land, together with a few implements and a team and some seed. The proportion of labor on a ranch to the value of the output is less than on a farm; therefore, the latter offers the better chance for the man whose initial capital is very small.

The opportunity for the beginner is generally in finding some rancher who wants to sell out, on terms, because of advancing age, or ill-health, or discouragement. In the last-named category one may be lucky enough to run across an Easterner or a townsman who had launched into the business with his judgment warped by reading too much western fiction or by seeing too many cowboy movies.

The question of land values then arises, and the proper approach is that used in appraising any business, namely: What income on the average will the investment produce? To answer that question we start with an appraisal of the carrying value of the land under consideration, and the yardstick for this is generally the number of acres necessary to run a cow-and-calf on a year-round basis. In the most favored districts this may be as low as eight or ten acres; in desert country it may be one hundred acres or even more. In our foothill belt, with rainfall, including the winter's snows, of about twenty-two inches, it is about fifteen. In the short-grass country to the east, across the intervening grain belt, where the rainfall is twelve inches or less it is generally taken as forty. In fixing this criterion of value, the hay land on which is grown the supplement of winter's grass is usually included, as is also the acreage necessary for the pasturage of the horses, saddle and draft. This meadow land or farming land is not usually measured and priced separately, but by its inclusion raises the general average of the whole tract. The tract under consideration should by all means have both hay land and grazing land; having discussed the considerations of balance between the two in Chapter I, I shall not go over the ground again.

The carrying value of any ranch may be ascertained by inquiry from the established ranchers of the district, preferably those not relatives or sidekicks of the prospective vendor. Professional agriculturists can be appealed to, such as the county agent or the officials of experiment stations, or of the state college of agriculture. These people are generally very willing to help the earnest inquirer. The figure to be sought is the long-term average, not what can be carried during seasons wetter than normal, and your inquiry should be specific in nature as there are sharp variations within any given district.

Having this figure, you are now, if you have a mind for that kind of thing, prepared to make a calculation. It may be interesting if I take you through such a process; I stress, however, the fact that my figures are in the nature of assumptions and should not be transferred bodily to the district you may have under consideration. Such variables as cattle prices, and wage levels, and feed prices, and distance from a loading point all enter into the computation of land values. I must of necessity make these assumptions; the calculations without them would be pointless.

Let us assume a carrying value of fifteen acres per head, and that you propose to run a cow-and-calf outfit, selling calves after weaning in the fall. The problem becomes extremely complex if you try to base a calculation upon multiple classes of livestock, such as purchased steers, your own steers, foundation females for sale, and a cow herd. I once turned an industrial cost accountant, a summer visitor, loose on my set of records, which are fairly complete, with instructions to allocate costs and profits between the various classes of my critters; he embarked upon the task with calm confidence, but two days later turned up with many foolscap sheets covered with figures and made the admission that the problem was the most intricate of any that he had encountered.

An average calf crop of 75 per cent is assumed. One cow therefore produces three-quarters of a calf on the average. Assume the value of the calf as an even $50. Applying to this the calf crop percentage of 75 per cent gives a value to the cow's annual production of $37.50. This value has to be adjusted to reflect your initial investment in the cow and her final beef value when she has passed the producing stage. Let us assume that you purchased the cow as a three-year-old, bred and about to drop her first calf. Her price at that time may be taken as $100. Let us further assume that her productive period lasts for ten years, at the end of which she sells (after a rest from breeding during which her carrying expense is not, for simplicity, counted) for $130. This figure presupposes a cow of excellent quality in good flesh; not all will be such, and some will die. This figure should therefore be discounted at least 15 per cent. The average salvage value for the old cow becomes thereby about $110. Since we have assumed that her value as a three-year-old bred heifer was $100, she has increased in worth over the ten-year period by $10, or at the rate of a dollar a year. This should be added to the value of her annual production, which, as we have seen, is $37.50. The sum is $38.50, which may be called the gross production value of the unit.

If, instead of having bought the cow as a bred three-year-old, you had raised her yourself, the computation will be somewhat affected by the deduction from her starting price of the amount of your profit in her at that time. If you priced her then at cost, you are not increasing your profit in her; you are merely deferring the realization of it.

This gross figure is sometimes used by the experienced stockman, who then divides it by the number of acres necessary to carry the cow, which gives him a gross land value to be used as a yardstick. This is done because the items of operating cost to be deducted from the gross figure vary so greatly in individual cases. This yardstick should not be used by the beginner, who should figure out his own annual operating expenses. The principal items of operating expense on a ranch are: hired help, taxes, interest, board of the men, gasoline and tractor fuel, purchased feed, machinery and truck upkeep and depreciation, fencing costs, expense for horses, depreciation on purebred bulls, upkeep and depreciation on buildings, veterinary and dipping expense, salt, seed, and shipping expense.

When these annual operating expenses have been totaled, we are in a position to carry our appraisal of land values to a conclusion. The total should be divided by the number of cows to be carried. The resultant figure is the cost of running one cow for one year, which prior to World War II was frequently taken in the West as $25. A cost study of fifty-five ranches in Utah made in 1925 by the Utah Agricultural Experiment Station * showed an average cost per cow of $23.90. Let us increase the $25 figure 18 per cent (ranching costs have not gone up quite so fast as industrial costs) and fix the figure at $29.50. Deducting this from the gross production value of the unit (as before given) in the amount of $38.50 leaves $9.00. Dividing this by fifteen (the number of acres necessary to sustain a cow on a year-round basis) gives 60 cents. This when capitalized at 10 per cent (a high rate but one comprising the inherent risk of drought, prairie fire, etc.) results in a value of $6 per acre. If all assumptions were as given, this is the amount the purchaser of a ranch could afford to pay, with the improvements, for his land. The price I have taken for livestock in this computation is on the high side, past experience considered, but I am assuming that costs of agricultural products are not coming down to where they were before the war, at least not for some time.

As it happens, the price I paid per acre for the last piece of grazing land, with a carrying value of fifteen acres to the head, that I purchased just before the war was $6 per acre. I should emphasize, however, that this was before ranchers generally began to realize that they have, in their trade, an ideal hedge against inflation, in that the value of their produce can be expected to go up proportionately to the general price level. They know also that they can themselves produce most of the necessities of life right at home.

Therefore to the calculated value of land, as above out-

* Wm. Peterson, *et al., Cattle Ranching in Utah.* Utah Agricultural Experimental Station Bulletin No. 203. November, 1927.

lined, one must concede that the holder can add an intangible value, and this will be reflected in the going price. This increment is now at least $2 per acre in our district, where ranches, however, are offered infrequently.

A calculation such as we have gone through may be of more academic than practical value under such unstable conditions as the present. It is, however, of value in showing where lies the limit on a strictly economic basis.

I referred in Chapter I to the advantage of so locating as to have access to supplemental grazing on government land. This should again be stressed here, for by such grazing the annual cost of running a cow is reduced. In the economic study of fifty-five Utah ranches referred to, the average annual cost of running a cow is given as $23.90. However, on thirty-six ranches using no public domain the cost averaged $30.52, and on the remaining nineteen the cost was $17.11. The difference in our region is not so great, but it is nevertheless substantial.

Grazing privileges on government land—the public domain —are secured from the Department of the Interior, through its Grazing Service, or from the Department of Agriculture, through its Forestry Service. These two departments promulgate grazing regulations that give the near-by established ranchers, either individually or organized into stock associations, the preference.

The areas administered for grazing are huge—that of the Grazing Service now consists of some one hundred and forty million acres. This is divided into sixty grazing districts, distributed throughout the states of Montana, Wyoming, Colorado, New Mexico, Arizona, Utah, Nevada, California, Oregon, and Idaho. Each of the sixty grazing districts has an elective advisory board, composed of local stockmen, and the allotment of grazing privileges, the seasons for use, and the total carrying capacity are fixed by the Grazing Service upon recommendation of these advisory boards.

Each district under this system therefore enjoys a large degree of autonomy, and the democratic procedure has obviated in large degree the intense, quarterless struggle for range grass between cattlemen and the range wars between cattlemen and sheepmen. The range, relieved from overgrazing by tramp graziers, has been largely restored to its former grass cover. The basic law governing these lands is a Congressional enactment known as the Taylor Act, and the areas affected are know as Taylor Act Land.

The Forestry Service of the Department of Agriculture administers the lesser areas suitable to grazing on forest reserves under regulations similar in nature to those of the Grazing Service. The grazing fees of both services are fixed in general at a very favorable figure—so favorable that proximity to, and a share in, such grazing confers a decided advantage upon the rancher who can qualify for participation. In effect, such a man has a vested interest in the public domain, and the value of his deeded land is enhanced thereby.

The wide grasslands of western Canada are similarly available to ranchers qualified by proximity, and are administered

by the Department of Lands and Mines of the prairie provinces, again at low fees.

It should be emphasized that nowhere are public lands
available for year-round grazing, nor can they serve solely to
sustain a ranching operation. They therefore do not afford
the newcomer an opportunity to get into the business on a
rental basis. They are considered as seasonal supplements to
base properties privately owned.

I can hear at this point some of my readers commenting
that if publicly owned grass is so valuable to the rancher he
ought to be made to pay more for it. To this I answer that
the grazing fees or lease rentals that the government gets
represent an out-and-out profit to it, the land being adaptable
to no other use, and also that if in the future the grazing
privilege becomes more valuable the going price will rise.
Leases granted to individuals or an association are not in general long-term, and are subject to competitive forces at re-
newal time; grazing fees are on an annual basis and can be
raised. The fact remains also that one cannot trail cattle too
far to public domain, because of the time involved, and the
shrinkage in weight of the animals, and the loss if cattle are
not closely watched. There is a limited market for such grass,
restricted to the ranches so located as to be able to take
advantage of it. And, candidly, there is also involved a mild
kind of subsidy toward a very necessary industry, one which
in many other respects is at an economic disadvantage.

❖

If the effect of such a computation as we have just gone through should be one of bewilderment upon the would-be rancher, I can say that there are many successful ranchers who would dismiss anything so involved as a bunch of turkey tracks. These are guided in their operations not by a set of books but by instinct, just as by instinct and not by compass the Cree Indian makes his way through the northern forests. The acquisition of such an instinct is not rapid and I do not recommend it in preference to a good set of records, but it can serve the same purpose. The men who possess it are in general those who have started in a small way and have kept the even tenor of their ways, not speculating or over-stocking.

In regard to speculation, this can be practiced in ranching as in any other trade. The method is to purchase, or to accumulate by withholding from market, cattle in anticipation of a rise in price. Such animals are, in the old Scotch phrase, kittle cattle; it is all right if you guess correctly, but if you do not, they can cause a lot of trouble. If the price turns downward you should sell and take your loss; this, however, goes against human nature, and so the speculator tends to keep his cattle on. If their number is greater than the natural carrying capacity of the ranch, the latter becomes overgrazed. If they are carried through a winter, the ranch's reserve of hay may be used up. An overgrazed pasture does not get back its cover for a long time, as the root system of the grasses is weakened. Weeds grow apace and the top soil is swept away by runoff water. There is no reserve of forage, and if the spring comes on dry, no new grass will appear.

By far the best way of managing your herd is to fix upon a safe, conservative stocking program, and keep to it through wet years and dry, through years of high prices and low. Adversity then will hold no terrors; you may have to do without many purchased items, but you will always have intact your breeding herd, which is your productive capital. You will always have, too, a reserve of hay, and in the spring pastures with good bottoms that will not burn up if the rains do not come. Good range husbandry in the long run produces better profits, and there is also satisfaction in knowing that the land is not being mined out, but preserved for the generations yet to come. Most stockmen have great respect for their grass cover, so much so that they are reluctant to break land and crop intensively for a few years that which nature intended for an ageless heritage.

I might here say that the system of rotational grazing, wherein a pasture is completely rested one year in four or five, used to be advocated by agrostologists; now, however, the practice is trending away from complete rest toward strict limitation of grazing for the selected year in the cycle. From observation over many years on our ranch I have found that more forage is produced that way.

Herd management and pasture management are in effect the two faces of the same coin. Overgrazing a pasture or stinting the feed in winter results in thin cows that do not catch as regularly as thrifty cows. Again I should like to speak of the importance economically of a high calf crop percentage. The condition of your summer and winter pastures has an important effect on it, in addition to the number and condition of your bulls, about which I have written in Chapter III. The mineral content of your forage should be studied, and if it is not up to the best standards, which on a range that has been grazed for many cattle generations is quite liable to be the case, supplements should be provided. You may disregard the claims of the many proprietary stock feeds; the minerals needed (in all except a small fraction of cases) are calcium, phosphorus, and iodine. In limestone regions cattle get enough calcium in the grass, but as the grass dries up it may become deficient in phosphorus. Inland areas such as the Great Plains usually lack iodine. As cold weather cames on we therefore make it a practice to give our herd iodine in the form of iodized salt, and we feed bone-meal (for phosphorus) in troughs placed near the watering places in the pastures.

To have a barren cow walking your pastures is like having an idle machine tool in the production line of a factory except that the idle machine does not draw power, but the cow does eat grass. The cost of carrying the fallow cow is exactly the same as that of the producing cow beside her; she adds to the total expense without furnishing any offset. It might be thought that since the beef value of a fat cow is normally greater than that of a heifer, as I have shown in my calculation of land value, she is increasing in value whether or not she produces a calf. This line of reasoning is fallacious, because at no time after she leaves the heifer stage is her annual increment in value equal to the cost of carrying her. Not a few stockmen fail to see this; they figure that as long as the cow is doing well she is making them money. This reasoning is correct when applied to steers up to the time they become three years of age, but it is not true of the herd matrons.

The beginner who has bought his land should, I believe, be in no hurry to stock it to the limit, particularly when, as at present, cattle prices are at a high level. Natural increase will soon furnish the desired numbers, and meanwhile he can better learn the details of herd management if he does not have too many animals to look after.

This counsel may seem to be in conflict with a theorem propounded by all writers on ranch economics. This is that the profitability of a ranch increases as the ratio of investment in cattle to investment in land and equipment increases. According to this doctrine, if there are two ranches of equal area, side by side, and stocked with the same number of cattle, the one having the lesser investment in land, buildings, and equipment will be the more profitable. This is correct as to a return calculated in dollars and cents, and the doctrine is valid for the man with strictly limited capital, one who must make every initial dollar count from the outset. It is unsound to have the value of cattle less than 35 per cent of the total invested capital. I may have been guilty in my chapter on the Ranch Homestead of placing too much emphasis on the ranch residence and its adjuncts. There is, however, a kind of return not calculable in dollars and cents, and this is the comfort and satisfaction of good ranch living. Under present conditions, where we have a highly technological society creaking in its many intricate parts, with even the experts disagreeing on where to make the adjustments and replacements, it is wise not to figure a ranch's returns solely in dollars and cents. The application of the owner's time and thought, and even of his excess dollars, will yield satisfaction in living, and when the time comes to retire this intangible reward may well be strongly reflected in the price he will receive.

✿

Once you have purchased and stocked your ranch, you then enter upon the operating stage, and in the long run you will stand or fall by the quality of your management. Providing the land is adapted to raising cattle, good management can overcome all other initial handicaps. Your management must not be, as I suggested at the outset of this chapter, either too casual or too painstaking. Either quality can very well put you out of business. The disadvantage of the former is obvious, that of the latter not obvious, but it can just as quickly lead to failure.

On a ranch a whole series of jobs always seem to be calling

for immediate attention. You will never get around to doing everything that needs to be done, and you must not fuss over unimportant things left undone. Every western ranch is always undermanned. One comes to envy the landed-proprietor-and-peasant system under which the foodstuffs of the Old World are produced, which makes possible sleek, well-kept, thrifty estates. On such there is always an abundance of labor because the people are retainers and attached to the soil. I do not know whether our system will, with the increase of population, ever come down to this; if it does, the time lies far in the future.

The rancher here never has time to do more than take care of the most urgent tasks, and he must learn to range these in their order of importance. In so doing he must relegate to an inferior position a host of appealing items. You have probably heard the story of the old farmer whose fields and buildings a professional agriculturist had carefully inspected. At the end of his survey, the agriculturist stopped the farmer in his plowing, and pointed out how this thing and that were not being done in the modern way. He offered to enlighten the farmer.

"Why, mister," answered the old man, "I ain't farming now half as well as I know how to."

In the single matter of livestock health the rancher never can do all the things that he knows would be advantageous. This feature exacts much time and expense, but the perfect state is never attained. For instance, a government pamphlet that I have on my table directed to the control of insect pests has a section relating to the horn fly. This states that the horn fly larvae hatch out in moist cow droppings, and if these dry out the larvae are killed. It winds up with the recommendation that cow pats be turned over with a shovel when dry on one side. It would take a perfervid imagination to see the rancher going about his pastures in the lee of the herds with a shovel. This had best be put down as a project for some future WPA, and allowed to rest there.

On the other hand, there are a number of feasible measures to improve livestock health which in the increase of insect pests that civilization brings in its train should not be neglected. One of these is the control of the warble fly. This fly causes great annoyance to cattle on summer days. It lays its eggs on the hair of the legs, and on the brisket. It is identical with the heel fly; cattle are terrified of it, and stampede wildly about the pastures when the fly is out, doing little feeding and losing much weight. The time for control is when the larvae are pupating in the cattle; at this time the grubs make their way from the intestinal tract to the back and loin, where they bore breather and exit holes in the hide, depleting vitality and spoiling the hide for leather. If at this stage the backs of the cattle be sprayed with a rotenone solution by means of a powerful machine sprayer, the grubs can be killed, and the life cycle of the pest interrupted.

Here is something important and practicable. Recently a

type of power sprayer adequate for the necessary high pressure has been developed, and has come to sell at a price that the stockman can afford. And also community sentiment has built up to a point where the ubiquitous recalcitrant, from whose untreated herd the fly could again spread, can be brought into line. Now this warble fly spraying comes in the spring of the year, when other tasks are urgent, and it is just one more thing to do, but it is so important that I move it to the top of the list, and therefore it gets done. Something else does not get done, such as putting new sills under the chicken house, or scything out the yard where the clothes are hung to dry, or cutting fireplace wood.

Week by week, month by month, season by season, there is this continuous process of appraising and readjusting the importance of the ranching tasks. Only a certain number of these can be fitted between the major jobs of the ranching years—the branding, the haying, the grain harvest, the fall roundup, and the winter feeding. The casual visitor to a commercial ranch is prone to mistake the disorder about the yard, the uncleaned corrals, the incomplete state of some structure for neglect, or even shiftlessness. If he were asked to appraise the relative success of two adjacent ranches he might give the palm to the one having the neater yard and the better kept buildings. The award should not be made, however, without an inspection of the herds and pastures; it might well be that the owner of the neater place is spending all his time around the yard, to the neglect of the earning assets. The corrals and yards of a ranch should be cleaned up and put in order, but only when there is nothing more important to do. During the intervals, the owner must reconcile himself to the unwilling violation of what is given (upon what authority I do not know) as Heaven's first law. Suburban prettiness is not attainable, and a ranch is no place for a perfectionist; such a one should become an artist, or a mathematician, or take a government job telling other people how to do things. Range country in itself seems to be stubbornly opposed to trimness. Its burning sun and strong winds will reduce all colors of paint to the same neutral gray; its winter snows and winds break off the limbs of carefully nurtured shade trees; the cattle will rub down such innovations as stiles and picnic tables; the sudden rainstorms will gutter footpaths and roadways.

If the owner of the ranch be the fortunate possessor of an outside income—a little of this will go a long way because fundamental wants are cheaply satisfied—he will be able to offset this effort of Nature to repossess her own, but if he has not he will have to roll with her punch.

The foreground of your vision may therefore be unkempt, and except when the wild flowers bloom there will be no sign of perfection. This will at times oppress the spirit of the gently nurtured. But such a one can always raise his eyes to the horizon, and if the perfection that there meets his gaze does not give a lift to his spirit, I suspect that he will find ranching no different in nature from the many vocations of the city within whose compass so many millions (in the phrase of Thoreau) lead lives of quiet desperation.

✿

The breeding and raising of cattle is, in spite of superficial appearances, an intensely competitive business. You are not in immediate and firsthand competition with your neighbors, as are the merchants fronting on Main Street. But the element is none the less ever present, and inexorable. Your product competes in the market pens with that of every other cattle raiser, be he farmer or rancher, within the marketing area. If you can raise a steer a little cheaper than your neighbor you will be gaining ground while he will be losing, and when a hard winter, or a parched summer, or a drastic price decline comes along you will be in the better position to survive.

Yours is a standard article of commerce, produced in large volume by tens of thousands of stockmen. Beef does not have to be constantly kept before the buying public by advertising, and the most intensive sales promotion campaign would do no more than raise a ripple on the vast sea of consumer demand. It is the housewife who sets its price, and she sets it in relation to that of all the other meats, and indeed to poultry and fish. Her morning scrutiny of the price list is the determinant. The packer has little to say; if she thinks that the price of beef is too high, and enough of her sisters agree with her, the sides of beef begin to back up in the packer's cooler, and to clear them he has to lower the price. If he has misjudged the market and has kept the price up too long his cut must be deeper than it otherwise would have been, and his order buyers in the stockyards get the word to take off a quarter, or even a half, instead of a dime. The stockman feels the effect at once. There is no use in his developing a grudge against the packer. This industry is more of a public utility than a private manufacturing business. It has to purchase everything that comes to the stockyards, whether it be a flood or a trickle. There may have been a time when the packer was a conspirator against the rancher's welfare, but I have seen nothing in my time to justify bringing in against him a true bill, although I, of course, share the usual and natural suspicion that develops in the breast of the raw material producer in relation to the processor of his product. I am content to leave the packers to the very complete surveillance of the various governmental regulatory bodies. I have lived in countries that have only the local buzzard-infested abattoirs where the meat has to be on its way to the consumers before it is cool, and I have come to classify the packer, with his elaborate system of refrigeration and distribution, as the ally rather than the antagonist of the livestock producer.

In beef we have, then, a commodity that is very sensitive to price, and that price is beyond the breeder's control, and beyond the feeder's and the packer's. Its cycles are much more nearly related to industrial activity than to cattle numbers, or any other supply factor. The supply of beef is never short, within the economic meaning of the term. The fluctuations in volume are never of the order of steel production, or of automobiles, or carloadings. This is probably because the trade is so sensitive to demand changes, and quickly readjusts its prices. It suggests the thought that it would be well economically if other commodities would develop similar sensitiveness, but unfortunately the trend seems to be in an opposite direction, and it takes something like a consumers' strike to correct overpricing.

The cattle producer is, then, never without a market. The public appetite gives beef the preferred position on the menu, and the housewife will consistently pay a higher price for it than for any other meat. Beef costs more to produce than any other staple meat, owing to the longer breeding cycle, and the slower rate of growth to a marketable age, but the preference persists in spite of the added cost. The average per capita consumption in the United States of all meats in the period 1900 to 1940 was 141 pounds, of which beef was 60.8 pounds, or 43 per cent. The consumption of meats from earlier years has been decreasing relatively, because of the entrance of new foods into the markets, but it has not, owing to the increase in the population, decreased in the absolute. In 1908, the high year of the period cited, the consumption was 162.6 pounds, of which beef was 44 per cent. In a recent five-year period (1935 through 1939) the per capita consumption had come down to 126.7 pounds, but beef, at 55 pounds, was still 43.5 per cent of the total. So our product is holding its own, and we do not have to fear, if past experience be any criterion, a failing of our market. There is some comfort for the future in the fact that the amount spent for food by the average American family is only 25 per cent of all expenditures, a ratio far lower than that in any other major country of the world, and we have withal a more ample and better balanced diet than any other country. There would seem to be some slack here in case of a decline in national income.

It is interesting, parenthetically, to note how the preference of people for beef manifests itself when price is not a consideration. On almost all ranches the family eats all the beef it wants. This is one of the perquisites of those in the business. On our ranch we are not confined to this one meat, for we have available pork, lamb (from neighbors), poultry, and game and fish in season. Under this virtually free choice, our average annual consumption per person of beef for a fair-sized family and the hired hands is about 150 pounds. The cattleman's imagination runs riot when he thinks of what would happen the nation over if this same condition were to prevail.

The breadth of the market for beef, while constituting an assurance of stability to the rancher, at the same time makes it virtually impossible for him to control the price. If all the ranchers of the great West were to organize a tight combine for the fixing of prices, this would fail to have any lasting effect, since the farmers of the nation raise an almost equal amount of beef. A survey of the geographical distribution of beef cattle will prove this point. For instance, Minnesota had in 1941 almost as many beef cattle as Montana—the figure for the former was 1,022,000 and for the latter 1,030,000. Missouri with 1,551,000 had more than Colorado with 1,137,000. Iowa with 2,938,000 had more beef cattle than any other state of the Union except Texas, which had 4,974,000. Many of the cattle included in the tabulation (which I have taken from the 1941 Reference Book of the American Meat Institute) were bred on the ranges and were in the process of being finished in the farm belt feed lots, but there are enough beef animals bred and grown out on farms to make valid my point, which is that the range man cannot have things his own way.

And in addition to cattle of the beef breeds, the supply of beef is augmented by the contribution of the dairy farmer, whose cull heifers, over-age milk cows, and calves go to the same markets as the beef cattle. They do not as a rule appear as roasts and steaks, but they are grist for the mechanical meat grinder, which very effectively does most of the chewing for the ultimate consumer, and the public appetite for hamburger is increasing.

The range critter is seldom now killed for meat before a final processing of greater or less duration in the feed lot, and the beef feeder is an intermediary between the breeder and the butcher. This trend toward grain finishing has both a favorable and an unfavorable effect upon the range industry. The favorable effect consists in the circumstance that the feeder stands ready to take the offerings of the rancher at the time when the high tide of marketing occurs, which is the fall of the year. He thus relieves the market from serious congestion. The unfavorable effect arises from the added increment of cost which his feeding, upon costly grains and hay, imposes. It would be a great boon to the range industry if a market could again be established for grass-fat beef. This used to prevail in the earlier years of the century, when consumption of beef per capita hit 70 pounds per year. There is some promise of its restoration in the attempt of the packers and the government during the war years to promote so-called utility beef. This effort would have more permanent effect if the surplus of the dairy herds did not somehow find its way into this category. Grass-fat beef of a tender and palatable nature, the kind reserved by the rancher for his own use, should be offered in much greater quantities. It is the foundation for the profitable Argentine beef industry, where but little beef is finished on grains. It will always be dollars per hundredweight cheaper than feed-lot beef. The rancher can make his contribution to this end by seeing to it that his animals are carefully grazed out and carefully handled to the shipping point. The packers can make theirs in promoting the idea by advertising and displays. The housewife can make hers by accepting beef that is not heavily covered with fat, and by waiving objection to the yellowish color of this fat. She must also be prepared to take heavier cuts of beef, since an immature animal, of the kind that is grain finished to make baby beef, does not get fat on grass alone.

While we are dealing with statistics, it would seem to be only fair to the prospective rancher to point out that the number of cattle at the end of 1944 had reached an all-time high in the nation's history, amounting to 82,000,000 animals. This figure comprises all cattle, milk and beef; it is probably the significant one for the student of ranch economics, because, as I have said, dairy stock ultimately finds its way to the butcher's counter. The entrance into any business at the high point not only in the cycle of available supplies but also of price might well be viewed with disapproval. There is only this to say on that score: This high point does not necessarily signalize danger for the *immediate* future, for much of the world has gone very hungry for long war years, and within our own boundaries people have not had during these years all the beef they wanted. If the management of our great public debt is sound, so that people will feel free to satisfy their accumulated wants from their savings, it would appear that industrial activity will continue for a certain number of years. The welfare of the cattleman is, as I have indicated, tied into the level of industrial activity more closely than into the special condition of his industry. It is likely that the surplus numbers (if surplus there is) of cattle can be drawn down quite rapidly.

There are all kinds and conditions of cattle, and the existence of this large number in itself implies that there are millions of head of the undesirable and uneconomical. The beginning rancher will do well to select as his foundation stock the highest quality of beef cattle, even if at first this means limiting the number of his productive units. The kind of cattle that has true beef conformation and that fleshes up rapidly on natural feeds is the kind to buy, or to raise. The established rancher will, I believe, be well advised to weed out the undesirables now while he has the chance to sell the culls.

✿

If, however, one has some reason to view favorably the immediate future, I believe that it would be self-deception to rest content in the belief that present beef prices will continue indefinitely. I am afraid that the long-term stabilization of any natural commodity at a high price level is beyond the power of man. I may be wrong, but the rancher sees too much of the ebb and flow of nature's forces and moods ever to have great faith in the doctrine of stability. He sees dry years succeed wet, and hard winters easy, and years in which, irrespective of rainfall, the cattle do better than in others. If he is of a philosophical turn of mind, he may also see that there are tides in the level of man's energies, and of man's morality. He might like to believe that his future can be made easy by the resolute pursuit of the doctrine of stability, but he has an ingrained skepticism about it, for it does not seem to square with nature's law.

He is conscious of the advantages being secured by urban labor with its tight organization, and of the rigidity of the prices of the manufactured articles he has to buy. He knows that he, together with his fellow workers in the field of agriculture, is now and ever will be in the minority. The very thrift and industry by which constantly increasing foodstuffs are turned out by a declining rural population militates against his cause. The rancher is an individualist, both by temperament and by reason of the isolation under which he lives; his voice is seldom raised in unison for the redress of economic inequity.

The consciousness that his hours of labor will never be greatly reduced, nor the prices that he receives ever be subject to his control, may at times arouse his ire, but it seldom oppresses his spirit. He will go on producing cattle and appraising horseflesh and admiring scenery until the mountains are made low and the rough places plain.

A friend told me a story that goes a long way in showing how the rancher looks at his trade. This man has a large urban business and had been telling me of the perplexities of administering it, and I had suggested that for relief he try my line. He pondered this a moment, and then said that he would not.

He had, it appeared, once been the guest of a railroad president on a private car, bound for a bird-shooting trip on the prairies of western Canada. The train had stopped at a cow town in eastern Alberta, where the rainfall is scanty, the grass short, and the winters long.

Two cattlemen in Stetsons and riding boots approached the brilliantly lighted car, which was hitched to the rear of the train. The summer, even for that country, had been dry, and the gait of the pair showed all too plainly that they had sought consolation in the bottle. As the leader attempted to mount the steps of the car the porter haughtily waved them away. The car, he said, was private. Chagrined, the cowman reflected a moment before retreating. He pointed to his companion in the shadows of the station.

"See that man?" he asked solemnly. "I'm a little fellow, but he's a big man in these parts. Lots of cattle. I knew him when he came here forty years ago. Didn't have a cent to his name. Now—" slowly and impressively—"*now he's almost out of debt!*"

# X. Conclusion

He causeth grass to grow for the cattle, and herb for the service of man; that he may bring forth food out of the earth.

Psalm 104

If in the preceding chapter I could not paint a future of flawless serenity for the business of the rancher, no more could I have done so, I imagine, for any other; I suspect that all of us, sooner or later, will have to pay for the vast destruction and wastage of these past years, and make atonement for the violence we have had to employ. The rancher will not be exempt in this process, and it would be a pusillanimous and probably a false counsel to present his trade as an island of tranquillity amidst the troubles that may be expected to come. To take to ranching merely because you expect to get out of something is not a valid reason for the choice. If you do not have your heart in it you will probably tire of it before the anticipated time, and you may not be able to attain before then the success necessary to survival.

There is an honestly earned peace of mind about it, however, when you are in the swing, and, although you cannot expect great riches to flow from it, there are many intangible rewards, some of which I have endeavored to set forth.

There is one on which I have dwelt lightly, and that is the quality of range hospitality. This is instinctive and uncalculating; the large rancher shows it to the small, and the small to the large. It is unrationed, in that you are welcomed for a day or a week; you need not fear to give offense by staying too long; indeed, you will be more likely to give offense by leaving too soon rather than too late.

Because of this spirit you can put a few articles in your saddlebags and hit out for a distant range, secure in mind as to shelter and food for yourself and horse. You need not stay on the roads, but can wander at will across meadows, prairies, and foothill spurs, and can spot from some butte or valley rim a habitation where, four out of five times, you will be welcome for the night. The fifth time you need merely move on to the next place. It is courtesy to help with the evening chores and the morning, and then to give your location as you move away. Your host may never drift over your way but he would like to know where you hail from.

The breadth of western hospitality brings in its train, as do all varieties of magnanimity, the possibility of abuse, and thus the newcomer to a ranching community may well find himself imposed upon by the grub-line rider. In every district there are one or two of these men who have no fixed abode and usually no trade, and ride from ranch to ranch, staying at each as long as their welcome holds out, a period fixed more or less by their capacity to entertain. The newcomer, not knowing his neighbors, naturally wishes to avoid giving offense, and so, until he gets his bearings, he has to chalk up to overhead the harboring of these men. They are as a rule a harmless lot, and in the process one can usually get some compensatory amusement.

Our first caller of this type was a middle-aged man, imposing in manner and speech, riding a double-rigged saddle with a martingale. He came just before dinner (on a ranch this is always served at noon) and received a cordial invitation. He stayed the afternoon, during which he talked at great length about the relationship of wars and sunspots, and in due course received an invitation to supper. As darkness was beginning to fall he said good-by and went for his horse, which he had tied to a fence post inside the horse pasture, in spite of our having urged him to put the animal in the barn. But the horse was not there; its halter rope had evidently come untied. There was nothing for it but that our guest should spend the night. The next morning he declined the loan of a mount, and when my hired man and I attempted to get his horse for him we found that it could no more be rounded up than a brush rabbit. It was a past master at playing ring-around-the-rosy in our willow and poplar brush. As we could not devote the whole day to the effort we came in, and found the owner eating an early dinner. He sunned himself throughout the entire afternoon, stayed for supper, and went out on foot to look for his horse, from which pastime he returned at a leisurely pace after dark, hungry and ready for a late snack. The next morning, when his breakfast had settled, he went out with a bucket of oats, which he said was sure to bring results, but the horse had evidently filled up on grass.

Finally, when it seemed that we would have him for the rest of the season, a neighbor came along who had the reputation of being an expert brush roper, able to throw the hooley-ann. I explained our predicament. Without a word he rode out with me; we located the horse, and he roped it. I thanked him, and not until then did he speak.

"That's about the tenth time I've roped that broom-tail. Next time Grub Line Jake comes along, watch how he ties his horse up. And you notice he's rigged up so's he won't lose his saddle."

Two months later we had our second call. The children and I sneaked out and looked at the imposing knot, seemingly secure, that held the horse to the post. One light pull at the halter shank and the knot dissolved. We retied with a bowline, but that evidently did not satisfy the hired man, for when Jake came out that evening to look for his horse he found that the halter shank had been spliced around the fence post.

Bill McIntyre tells of another instance of an unwelcome guest over at his big I H L outfit. There the foreman's daughter did the cooking for the crew. She was neat and pretty and an extraordinarily good cook. A cowpuncher from a neighboring ranch took to sparking her regularly each Saturday night. He was a real dresser, rode a Sunday horse, and was what the cowboy calls a shadow rider. There is no cheval glass on a ranch, and none in the cow-town hotels, and so the puncher who wants to admire himself full length has to do so by watching his shadow as he rides along.

The ardent suitor came to be looked upon by the bunk-house crew with intense dislike, and when he appeared one evening clad in dove-colored, choke-bore pants (i.e., jodhpurs) they took action. They found a can of red paint, and after dark painted the seat of his saddle. At long length he came out and mounted and rode away. As luck would have it that was the night when he forgot some of his jewelry; he soon reappeared and went into the house. A piercing feminine shriek rent the night air; he came out on the prod, and if he had been packing a gun there would have been murder.

I think that you can imagine what his nickname was from then on.

✿

A ranch, or a farm for that matter, is a pretty good place to bring up a family, the relationship between members of a family being one of mutual dependence. Each child is a partner in the family institution, and each has a contribution to make according to his age and capacity. The child does not play at helping his parents; effect and cause are in obvious relationship, and if the cows go unmilked, the chickens unfed, and the garden untended the family fortunes suffer. Children can greatly improve the standard of living on a ranch, for there are many time-consuming chores, well within their capacities, which when performed enhance the standard of living. The older boys can be of real help to their father in field and herd management. A fifteen-year-old boy brought up on a ranch is worth more than a thirty-year-old greenhorn; he can drive the truck and the tractor, and take a man's place, in all respects except the infrequent roping, at working and driving cattle. A daughter can be of equal help to her mother in providing the material comforts, and in bolstering the ambitions and standards of the males. The association between parents and children is much closer than in the city; the children can see how the father makes the living of the family, and the relationship of the essential skills to success, and they become the more willing to learn. On the side of the parents not only is there the material help of which I have spoken, but there is the gift of companionship and the brightening of their vision.

The essential skills and lessons of conduct need not be taught with a heavy hand. With a little ingenuity many of the ranch jobs can be made into expeditions for the whole family; for instance, the menfolk can take a bunch of cattle to an outlying pasture and the womenfolk can take the necessary salt in the pickup truck to an agreed-on meeting place, where there is water and wood. There the picnic supper is eaten, while the hobbled horses munch grass and the camp-fire dances skyward, and tales are told of the long ago when the Blackfeet were masters of prairie and foothill. There are also camping trips to the mountains for the cutting of corral poles, and there are trips to look at saddle horses, and pure-bred bulls. There is the treat of a trip to the city with, coming and going, visits to ranching friends.

It is a wise father who fortifies his sons against the hazards of life by teaching them a trade. On this foundation there can be erected the superstructure, if circumstances permit and the boy is qualified, of academic or professional educa-tion. Modern ranching is in part a composite trade, put together from fractions of many other trades. There is in it some carpentry, some blacksmithing, a little of mechanics, a lot of field husbandry and animal husbandry. The rancher can instruct his sons in all that he knows of these, and the gaps in his knowledge can often be supplied in the process of trading work with a neighbor. But if ranching is in part a composite trade, it is for the rest a particular trade, with skills and lore of its own. These skills the boys will pick up in proportion to their natural agility and daring.

Lest I may have given the impression, in the endeavor to define the minimum requirements for the beginner in the ranching business, that these special skills are to be depre-cated, I hasten to make disavowal. If it is a choice for the beginner between riding a plug or going afoot, and between using a ground loop and letting an animal go uncaught and untended, I say take the ignominy of the lesser course in your stride. Although the beginner may have to forgo the acquisition of the highest order of riding and roping skills, his boys need not. Indeed, one cannot keep them from it, and it will not be long until they know the style of every good bucking horse in the country—whether it be sunfishing, head swallowing, sulking, crawfishing, rainbowing, or windmilling.

On the subject of roping they will acquire very definite ideas, and if their father has no opinions of his own they will be supplied him after the boys have attended their first two or three rodeos. It will not be long thereafter until there develops an argument between a young tie-fast man and a dally man—the former method is, I might explain, to use a short light rope tied fast to the horn; the latter, a longer rope which when the catch is made is dallied (wrapped) about the horn. There will also be arguments between the merits of forefooting and neck roping, and between a narrow and a wide, or Mother Hubbard, loop, and between a standing loop throw—the California twist—and a twirled throw.

The acquisition of these and kindred skills, and their perfection, can make the trade into a fine art, and it is well not to discourage the boys in their pursuit, even if in the process you have to be witness to a few hard spills. It is well also to encourage the youngsters in the pursuit of the gentler skills of the business, such as the judging of horseflesh and of cattle. It is particularly important that the boy develop an eye for cattle, and the best way to do this is to give him a few cows of his own, the produce of which he is free to keep for himself. No means more sure to enlist his interest can be devised, nor for developing his eye for conformation and thrift. His cows should always be run in the main breeding herd, so that in looking over the bunch for his own he will survey all. A man raised with cattle develops the faculty of taking in many points at a glance, whereas the man not so brought up has to look each time he wants to note some particular feature, such as condition of flesh, or age, or the presence of strays. To the novice it is astounding what a good stockman sees when riding through the herd. In the difficult matter of getting a count he can often tell you, after the cattle have filed through a gate, not only the number of head but the approximate division of the herd by sex, and the number in each age group.

The highest branch of animal husbandry is in raising purebreds. If a boy has a particularly good eye for cattle, it is well to direct his attention to this kind; if you do not run registered cattle yourself you can take him on trips to buy your bulls, and to stock shows. He can be supplied with the trade magazine of one of the breeds and can be given books dealing with the subject.

Between play and chores and the acquisition of new knowledge time never hangs heavy on children's hands. There is no need for the many organizations and activities to which children in a city are committed for their spare time. These in themselves are no doubt excellent, but the country dweller is appalled by their multiplicity and wonders at a system of life wherein leisure is so abundantly created that only the most strenuous efforts and the most extensive organization are able to cope with the problems it creates.

I probably do not need to tell you that in the process of training and conditioning your children you will derive reciprocal advantage, not the least of which will be to see the world about you through young eyes. You will not be allowed to view prairie and foothill and mountains perfunctorily, as a man does the walls of his office, nor will you be permitted to lose entirely your sense of wonder at the ever-changing manifestations of nature.

> Up to the cornfield, old and curly,
> I took Joe, who rises early.
> Joe, my yearling, on my shoulder,
> Observed the old corn growing older.
> And I could feel the simple awe
> He felt at seeing what he saw.
> And being present at the birth
> Of my child's wonderment at earth,
> I felt my own life stir again
> By the still graveyard of the grain.*

❖

* From *The Fox of Peapack,* copyright, 1931, by E. B. White; published by Harper & Brothers.

I have perhaps reversed the natural order by discussing the manner in which the rancher should manage his children before discussing the manner in which he should manage his wife. There is little to say upon this subject; the association is such that little management by either party is required. There is a natural division of labor that promotes reciprocal dependence, and from reciprocal dependence flow understanding and sympathy.

In the first place, the wife has, in recognition of her equal status, a proud position on a ranch. Her title is officially that of "The Missus." Though the gently reared woman may at first regard this with aversion, she comes before long to take pride in it. As the Missus she commands the respect of the ranch hands, the neighbors, the tradesmen in town, and the visitors. Her word in regard to anything pertaining to the distaff side is law, whether it be in connection with provisioning, gardening, the poultry flock, the reliability of the children's school horses, or what kind of work can be done on the Sabbath. In large part she sets the tone of the ranch's relationship with the neighbors, and despite the most judicious handling of labor relationship by the boss, it is her cooking and her spirit that determine how long the men stay. She is the nurse of the sick and injured.

The provinces of husband and wife are sharply defined, but, since they work shoulder to shoulder, each has an understanding of the problems of the other. The working of cattle in the corrals, the breaking of colts, the feeding in winter—

all take place, if not before her eyes, at least where she is cognizant of them. And when a cattle or horse buyer comes to the ranch, he will usually stay to a meal, and she will hear discussed such matters as weights and shrink and prices. The talk of the boss and his men around the table will keep her informed of the checker game that is pasture management. She will see her husband at his accounts, and may be asked to check the sums.

The bond is strengthened by the fact that so many of the needs and comforts of the husband are provided directly by his helpmeet, and not by agencies and institutions hired to replace her. There is little eating out; clothes cannot be sent out to a laundry; the flowers that brighten the house are home-grown, not sent from a florist's. The poultry for the table runs around with feathers on until the hour of doom; the milk comes warm from the dairy, in pails, and does not become butter, cream, cottage cheese, and buttermilk until it passes through her hands. She literally keeps the home fires burning, and there is no greater pleasure than to ride over the rimrock on a winter's evening and see shining warmly on snow or frosty grass the lights of home, and sniff the wood smoke that is wafted to your nostrils, and to know that within security and warmth and affection await.

There is not the divorcement between the making and the spending of money that there is in the urban household. It is, after all, a whole lot easier for a woman to understand the business of breeding, raising, fattening, and selling livestock than such matters as factory production and design changes; of sales promotion and trade territories and distributor margins and traffic; of financial statements and credit ratings and insurance and income-tax accounting. Such are usually Greek to her, and her husband does not have time to teach her Greek, since she sees him but a short time in the morning, when he is too preoccupied to talk, and at night, when he is too tired. The trips she and her husband take together may be directed to business ends rather than to recreation. The same may be said, of course, for many of the ranch trips, such as the cutting of poles in the mountains or the journeys to purebreds sales, but here at least the wife is abreast of her husband's reasons and purposes. Her suggestions are entitled to receive, and do receive, respect.

The interdependence of husband and wife enforces consultation, whether or no there be a disposition thereto, and there will not be many decisions taken without concurrence. These decisions will range from the casual to the important—from such matters as what beef to kill to the question of whether to purchase more land. As to premises such decisions may be simple, but they will be of importance as to results. The sums involved may not be large, judged by the standards of business, but they are personal in nature and if a mistake be made it will not be lost in corporate profit and loss, or be borne in part by the collector of internal revenue.

The same interdependence and close association can, of course, in cases where the partners are profoundly antipathetic, operate to make the institution of matrimony a tougher ordeal on a ranch or farm than in a city. There is little chance for husband and wife to get away from each other. Accordingly, ranch living is balm in those fissions where there is maladjustment and petty misunderstandings arising from divergent points of view and interests, but salt where there is antagonism. But, strangely, even in such cases the expedient of divorce does not often seem to be invoked by country people; they apparently try to fight it out for a while and then take refuge in silence. I suppose that every farm district and every range area has an example or two of husband and wife who have not spoken to each other for ten, or twenty, or thirty years, or even longer. Strangely enough their places are not always the unthriftiest in the district, nor are they shunned by neighbors, who learn to make allowances.

The example of such couples is salutary, particularly upon young couples just starting out. There should be, on a ranch, play periods together, however brief and unscheduled. The husband should see to it that the wife has at all times a good horse, gentle and lifey, and so mounted that she gets away from the routine of the home. It takes persuasion to get ranch women on horseback—range tradition is senselessly against it—but the reward is worth the effort. The range then lays its hand, a gentler hand, upon them too.

They also come to know that distances are great, and that ranch work cannot be rigidly scheduled, and that the husband must miss some of the carefully prepared meals and come home late to others. Thus this single most disruptive circumstance in the marital relationship is robbed of its malevolence.

All in all, I should say that the two greatest benefits of true country living are, in inverse order of importance but in direct order of occurrence, physical well-being and domestic harmony.

✿

The West once had its troubadours, working cowpunchers who traveled with a guitar slung over their shoulders. They were everywhere welcomed, and enlivened many an evening around the campfire or the kitchen stove. Since the advent of the radio and the movies they have largely deserted the range for the studios. There they seem to be doing very well for themselves, lamenting, sometimes very tunefully, the passing of the open range. Their string of songs has been enlarged, and greatly improved, by the efforts of the professional song writers, most of whom, I am told, would not be able to tell the difference between a pair of chaps and a pair of taps. There should be no objection to this circumstance; I would take, any time, "Home on the Range" or "Give Me My Boots and Saddle" in preference to "Bury Me Not on the Lone Prairie" or the interminable "Billy Venero."

The present-day rancher does not, however, take their plaints very seriously. The West is now more habitable; there are more families making an adequate living; there are more cattle, and very much better cattle. There are schools for the children; there is the telephone, which saves endless miles of travel; there is the radio, and, most transforming of all, there are roads and cars. The doctor can now reach you when sickness or injury strikes, and a trip to town to stock up is a matter of hours instead of days.

Some of the romance may have vanished, but the rancher is better off on balance, and knows it, and does not regret the passing of the Old West oftener than a score, or possibly two score, times a year, when for instance he has to fix a long line of fence, or hoe up the garden, or when he gets his tax statement, or draws rein on some hilltop when there is a cool wind blowing from the north.

His conveniences and comforts exact a price, as I have endeavored to show. He will work somewhat harder than the old-timer—not harder than the latter used to work at such times as the spring and fall roundups—but he will put in more hours the year round.

Some of these excess hours are entailed by the necessity of raising a better class of cattle than the old-timer raised, but many of them are simply the cost of an enhanced standard of living, coupled with the disappearance of low-priced help. It is entirely possible to dispense with the amenities and improvements that exact such extra hours. The business is less inflexible than, let us say, keeping a store on Main Street.

There are many ways of managing a ranch, almost as many

in fact as there are ranches. No two places are exactly alike, differing as to topography, as to soil, as to grass cover. You will have more ways of living and working than can be compressed within the covers of a book.

Underlying all ways there is one cardinal principle: live on good terms with the land. This in essence means that you must not abuse the grass cover. Depend on it for your principal sustenance; you may break small areas of sod, with due regard to loss of soil fertility, soil drifting, and erosion, but do not make the mistake of sending feed off your place other than on the hoof.

The grass cover is the natural heritage of the successive generations, and by it you may in your time, season after season, "bring forth food out of the earth."

And now it is time to swing the gates of the corral shut on these random thoughts. As I write it is greening-up time, the best of all seasons on a ranch. The herd matrons stand knee-deep in the new grass, chewing the cud of contentment, while their offspring runs stiff-legged about them, shying at sun splotches and butting at butterflies. The sun is genial in its warmth, but the mountains still have their snowcaps. The river is bank-full, and the rivulets in the pastures tinkle over their pebble beds. The procession of the wild flowers has begun. Ahead there stretch the tasks of another ranching year, its start soon to be signalized by the spring branding.

We view with serenity this coming year, and those thereafter that may be allotted to us, and we wish all, east and west, north and south, who are our fellows, and all who may wish to throw in their lot with us: Good grass, heavy weights, and a clean gather!

**THE END**

# Bibliography

The reader who wishes to go further into the details of modern ranching may find, as I have, the following books and pamphlets of value.

*Livestock Husbandry on Range and Pasture* and *Range and Pasture Management,* by Arthur W. Sampson, published by John Wiley & Sons. These books, companion volumes, deal with the practical operations of ranching and with the body of scientific knowledge, such as parasitology, toxic weeds, bovine diseases, grazing methods and agrostology, built up by the professional agriculturists.

*Range Beef Production,* by Fred S. Hulz, published by John Wiley & Sons. This is an eminently practical exposition of prevailing practice. It has much material on the economics of beef production.

*Modern Beef Cattle Breeding and Ranching Methods,* by Wallis Huidekoper. This is in pamphlet form and is published by the Montana Stockgrowers Association at Box 864, Helena, Mont. It presupposes some knowledge of the business on the part of the reader, and is greatly condensed. It is the best short account, all in all, that I have seen.

*The Cattle King,* by Edward F. Treadwell, published by The Macmillan Company. This is the story of one of the great cattle kings of the West, Henry Miller, of California. I have put it on my list not because it is particularly relevant to the operations of the small or medium-sized ranch, but because it is the only factual, methodical, and clear exposition that I have encountered of the rise of a cattle baron to fortune. There are no cattle wars, no shooting affrays, no political shenanigans; the manner in which the empire was built up was that of patient, methodical, step-by-step advance.

*Beef Cattle Production in the Range Area,* one of the Farmer s Bulletin Series of the U.S. Department of Agriculture. A sound, somewhat condensed, exposition of the subject. All ranchers should have the check list of titles in the series of Farmer's Bulletins. This may be had by writing to the Department at Washington. Many of these bulletins are directed to the activities of the womenfolk, such as those on gardening, the poultry flock, home preserving, etc. A word of warning as to those bulletins dealing with ranch structures: we find that for our large northern cattle the sheds and barns are seldom shown large enough for their rated capacity, and handling structures, such as chutes, are not designed with heavy enough materials.

*The Western Horse,* by John A. Gorman, published by The Interstate. A concise treatise on the selection, training and care of the western cow horse.

*Western Words,* by Ramon F. Adams, published by the University of Oklahoma Press. A glossary of ranching words and phrases, leavened by western humor.